The American Vision

Performance Assessment Activities and Rubrics

Glencoe McGraw-Hill

New York, New York   Columbus, Ohio   Chicago, Illinois   Peoria, Illinois   Woodland Hills, California

To The Teacher

This *Performance Assessment Activities and Rubrics* booklet for *The American Vision* serves two purposes. It is an alternative form of assessment, but it is also an alternative teaching technique that uses a "hands-on" approach to student learning. Performance activities require students to actually use the concepts they are studying to complete a project for an audience. Performance activities ask students to communicate information to others through some form of media. In effect, students demonstrate and increase their understanding and mastery of the material by being asked to teach it to others.

Creating a Customized File

There are a variety of ways to organize Glencoe Social Studies teaching aids. Several alternatives in creating your own files are given below.

- Organize by category (all activities, all tests, etc.)

- Organize by category and chapter (all Chapter 1 activities, all Chapter 1 tests and quizzes, etc.)

- Organize sequentially by lesson (activities, quizzes, tests, for Chapter 1/Section 1, Chapter 1/Section 2, etc.)

No matter what organization you use, you can pull out individual worksheets from these booklets for your files, or you may photocopy directly from the booklet and file the photocopies. You will then be able to keep the original booklets intact and in a safe place.

Glencoe/McGraw-Hill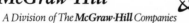
A Division of The **McGraw·Hill** *Companies*

Send all inquiries to:
Glencoe/McGraw-Hill
8787 Orion Place
Columbus, OH 43240

ISBN 0-07-828068-0

Printed in the United States of America

1 2 3 4 5 6 7 8 9 10   066   08 07 06 05 04 03 02

Table of Contents

Performance Task Assessment Lists and Scoring Rubrics

The Performance Assessment System

BENEFITS OF PERFORMANCE ASSESSMENT

A common model of assessment is to teach the chapter, stop, and test the students. Performance assessment changes this pattern. With performance assessment, *The American Vision* becomes a learning resource—a means to an end rather than the end in itself.

When students leave school, they will use books and other sources to find information. Performance assessment tasks use information as it is used in the larger world. Schoolwork becomes valid preparation for life outside the classroom. Teachers guide, provide models of excellence, and give feedback each step of the way. (See the flowchart for information problem solving on the next page.)

Performance Assessment Looks at Authentic Use of Information

Performance assessment is not a testing strategy, but a way of teaching and learning that integrates process and product. Effective teaching, meaningful learning, and motivation all play a role in planning and carrying out performance assessment. The performance assessment tasks in this booklet combine historical information and concepts with interdisciplinary tasks. Each performance task involves students in developing processes and crafting products for specific audiences.

Performance Assessment Tasks Require Thinking Skills

Thinking skills provide the "verbs" that direct the action in performance assessment tasks. The tasks involve:

1. **Getting the information** (finding, collecting, reading, listening, observing).

2. **Working with the information** (comparing, contrasting, classifying, inferring, analyzing, synthesizing, generalizing, evaluating, making models, and/or reasoning).

3. **Using the information for a purpose** (informing, persuading, motivating).

4. **Using the information to craft a product/ presentation** (speaking, writing, designing, constructing, demonstrating).

5. **Using information to communicate with specific audiences** (peers, younger, older, informed, diverse groups).

Performance Assessment Involves Cooperative Learning

Cooperative learning is valuable in the larger world. Businesses seek employees who establish and maintain positive working relationships with others. Cooperative learning stimulates the business environment. Performance assessment often uses a combination of individual and group learning activities. Group work in the initial step actively involves students and stimulates them to share ideas. When groups complete the entire project, individuals should be accountable for specific tasks, and each student should assess his or her own work. There is no group grade. (See the rubric for a Cooperative Group Management Plan on page 81.)

THE PERFORMANCE ASSESSMENT SYSTEM

Each part of the performance assessment system has a specific function. The central task requires the use of information, concepts, skills, and attitudes. The rubrics and performance task assessment lists guide and evaluate the process and product. The models of excellent student work provide clear targets of quality and help students learn independently.

The Performance Task

For each chapter in *The American Vision*, you will find performance assessment tasks. Use them as suggested, or change them to meet the individual needs of your students. With experience, students will be able to help create their own original activities.

Format of a Task The first step in creating a performance assessment task is to identify the main concepts and thinking skills you want to be the targets of the assessment. You may not give the task a title until later. In a few words, state the background of the concept (Federalists and Antifederalists, for example). Next, consider what product you want students to make. You may give students options or let them select the format for the product. The audience, too, may be left up to the students, or you may select one for them. After students know the product and the audience, help them identify the product's purpose. Will it inform, persuade, and/or motivate the audience?

The next step involves writing the procedures. First you may want to set the scene by giving the

INFORMATION PROBLEM SOLVING

ASK QUESTIONS

↓

UNDERSTAND THE TASK
- Select a reasonable and focused topic.
- Know the purpose of the product.
- Understand how the product will be presented.
- Identify the audience for the product.

↓

SURVEY EXISTING KNOWLEDGE AND PREPARE FOR NEW LEARNING
- Summarize what is known.
- Outline what needs to be learned.
- Identify information sources.
- Prepare a task/time management plan.

↓

RESEARCH THE SELECTED TOPIC
- Use a variety of quality information sources.
- Collect and organize information.

↓

CONSTRUCT A PRODUCT
- Writing
  - Reports
  - Journal Entries
  - Scripts
- Oral Presentations
  - Monologues
  - Skits
- Visuals
  - Drawings
  - Models
  - Bulletin Boards
  - Maps
  - Graphs
  - Mass Media

↓

ASSESS THE WHOLE PROCESS
1. Identify strengths and weaknesses of the process.
2. Identify strengths of the final product.
3. List goals to improve future work.

The American Vision

students some background information about the concept. The directions can be very specific or very open depending on the degree of structure the students need.

Finally, give the students some guidelines about the assessment. Explain that they will use performance task assessment lists and that the teacher will keep the grades and other official information; the students should keep a log of the tasks they complete.

Individual Log   If students have the freedom to choose the task, and/or the purpose, and/or the audience, they should keep individual records of tasks they need to accomplish. Students should mark the tasks they choose to save in a working folder so they will have them when they make the final selections for their portfolios. Information in a student's log should include name, task title, type of product, audience for the task, purpose of the task, date completed, and overall self-assessment.

Using Performance Assessment Tasks

The tasks in this book may be easily adapted by changing the product, purpose, and/or audience. Find audiences for the products and performances of your students. Audiences can include other students, citizens in the community, and parents and other adults. Involving outside audiences adds authenticity to the students' work.

Start Slowly and Go One Step at a Time   You may begin by choosing just one performance assessment task. After some experience, you may want to add others. Another strategy is to give the students a menu of performance tasks early in the course, and let the students select one or two to do as major products for the course. At set times in the course, students present their products or performances to the class. If the students' tasks call for an outside audience, allow that experience to occur first. Then, when a student reports to his or her peers in history class, the experience with the outside audience can be part of the report.

Use Performance Task Assessment Lists and Models of Excellence   At the beginning of a performance task, show students the relevant performance task assessment list. Also show them examples of excellent work that is similar, but not identical to, their current project. If you do not have models of excellent work available at first, you and your colleagues can define what excellent work is for the course.

Students in subsequent classes will learn to use both the performance task assessment lists and the examples of excellent work from previous students to guide their work. Discourage copying. As students create new projects, you can add them to others in the set of benchmarks.

Assessing Tasks

Using rubrics and performance task assessment lists, focus student attention on how the performance tasks help build literacy in American history.

What is a Rubric?   A rubric is a set of guidelines for assessing the quality of a process and/or product. The rubric includes a continuum of quality—from excellent to poor. There are many varieties of rubrics. This book uses a six-level rubric, known as the "Two-Decision Rubric."

Using the Rubric   To use the rubric, the teacher studies the product and makes the first of two decisions. Is the product more like one that is excellent (T)* or more like one that is poor (W)? If the product is more like a T, then the teacher makes the second and final decision. Is the product unusually excellent (S), evenly excellent (T), or mostly excellent (U)?

If the first decision is that the product is more like a W, then the teacher decides if the product is evenly poor (W), mostly poor but with some better elements (V), or not done or very poorly done (X). After just two decisions, the teacher places the product on a six-point scale:

---

*Rubrics in this book use letters instead of numerals so that teachers are not tempted to average the scores. The scores of 1, 2, 3, and 4 do represent a continuum of quality, but the degree of difference between each of the numbers is equal. Rubrics are more like Continuum B than Continuum A in the following illustration. Adding these unequal values together to calculate a "mean" score is essentially meaningless.

Continuum A
Equal intervals between values:
1 2 3 4

Continuum B
Unequal intervals between values:
1 2 3 4 5 6

Consider these ratings made by a student on seven posters done throughout the course:

W   U   T   U   U   T   T

It would be correct to describe the student's long-term performance by reporting that he or she made three Ts, three Us, and a W. The T ratings at the end show that the student improved with time and practice.

	Superb, eloquent, unusually excellent
Y	Evenly excellent
U	Unevenly excellent, one or two important elements are not excellent
V	Better than poor, one or two important elements are better than poor
W	Evenly poor
X	Not done or very poorly done

7. What helps you be creative?

8. What are three words that describe you as a student? Explain how those three words best describe you.

9. If a camera were taking pictures of you working on this project, what would it see?

10. Name the person who was the biggest help to you on this project. How did he or she help you?

11. How does this project show that you really understand the concepts of American history?

12. How does this project show that you are making decisions to improve your understanding of American history?

If two or more teachers evaluate the same performance or product, such as a poster, then using the same rubric will help them both view it in the same way. Once a rubric is complete, many teachers can use it unaltered.

Performance Task Assessment Lists   Teachers devise performance task assessment lists as guidelines for students. With experience, students working individually or in groups can make their own assessment lists—and that involves them more actively in their own learning.

Students' Self-Assessment   The ability to self-assess and plan for improvement is a valuable life skill that performance assessment fosters. Students evaluate their work, identifying parts that are done well and those needing improvement. They use performance task instructions, the performance task assessment lists, and the models of excellence as tools to improve their work.

Helping Students Become Better at Self-Assessment   If the students are not experienced in self-assessment, they will need training. After students complete tasks, ask them to respond to the following questions so that they will gain experience with self-assessment.

1. What do you like most about your (product)? Why?

2. What was the most difficult part of making the (product)? Why?

3. If you were to do this project again, what would you do differently? Why?

4. If you were to revise this project one more time, how would you change it and why?

5. How did you craft your project so that it would be just right for the (specific audience)?

6. Describe a situation when you got stuck and were frustrated with the project. What helped you get going again?

Audience Assessment   Many of the performance tasks target an audience other than the classroom teacher. If possible, the audience should give the author feedback.

The Portfolio

Portfolios are a good way to look at a student's overall work. Take care not to just collect items, place them in a folder, and call it a portfolio. Plan portfolios with student benefits in mind. One strategy is to have students save a variety of their best works. Near the end of the course, the teacher asks the students to select a small number of products that contributed to their total American history literacy.

When the students have made their selections, they each write a narrative explaining why they chose those particular items and how those items demonstrate their understanding of American history. The teacher reads the students' narratives and writes short responses. The portfolio and student narrative figure significantly in the students' final grade. This portfolio strategy engages the students in decision making, promotes self-analysis, and requires a reasonable amount of work from the teacher.

If you plan to use the portfolio, explain this assignment near the beginning of the course. Focus on the idea that the portfolio will be a small collection of a variety of items that will demonstrate how much the student has learned about American history.

Some items, such as written reports, journals, scripts, and booklets fit easily into a portfolio folder. Other items, such as posters and bulletin board displays, may be too large. If possible, students should keep photographs of their very best works that do not fit into the portfolio.

Grades

You may need to give students grades for their projects. On each performance task assessment list there is an opportunity for you to assign a point value to each element on the list. You and the student award points according to the quality of the work relevant to that element.

Using This Book

This booklet contains performance tasks for use with each of the 34 chapters of *The American Vision*. Note that the procedure found in each performance assessment refers students to particular task assessment lists. To guide you in your assessment of a task, use the corresponding rubric. A convenient list located near the top of each rubric and performance task assessment list identifies a particular performance assessment activity. You may wish to adapt the rubrics and performance task assessment lists to meet your own needs.

★ Performance Assessment Activity 1

Use with Chapter 1

Early Americans

✪ BACKGROUND

No one knows for sure when the first people arrived in America. Most scientists believe that the first Americans appeared between 15,000 and 30,000 years ago. These people were probably hunters who had to move from place to place in order to find food. After a time, these Native Americans learned how to plant and raise crops. Because people needed to stay in one place to tend their crops and store their harvests, their nomadic way of life gradually changed. The first permanent villages were established. These early cultures—the Hohokam, the Anasazi, the Adena culture, the Hopewell culture, and the Mississippian culture—gave way to later settlements in what we now call the United States.

Depending upon the climate and the abundance of game, people living in these later settlements sometimes combined hunting and farming. The Inuit and the Aleut settled in the Far North. Because of the climate, these people depended heavily upon hunting for their livelihood. Farther inland, groups such as the Ute and Shoshone lived a nomadic life because the land was too arid for farming. In the Southwest, the Zuni, Hopi, and Pueblo peoples grew several species of corn. Sometime around the 1500s, the Apache and the Navajo also settled in the Southwest. Some of the Apache peoples were nomadic hunters, but the Navajo learned to farm from the Pueblo people. In the Great Plains, the Pawnee, Kansas, and Iowa peoples continued to farm and to hunt. In the Eastern Woodlands, early peoples combined hunting and fishing with farming. Native Americans living east of the Mississippi River and south of the Great Lakes supported themselves by hunting and farming. By the 1500s, Native Americans had developed economies and lifestyles based on the geography and climate in their particular parts of North America.

✪ TASK

You are going to create a map that shows the early Native American settlements in North America. On your map, include civilizations that existed in North America between 3000 B.C. and the A.D. 1500s. You will make a legend for your map that identifies economic and cultural forces that were in effect in each civilization.

✪ AUDIENCE

You work for a Native American Cultural Center. The map will be read by visitors to the center.

✪ PURPOSE

The purpose of this activity is to provide a visual presentation of the geographic location and economic and cultural forces in North America during a specific time period. By looking at your map, you will gain a better understanding of how economic and cultural forces changed over time.

★ Performance Assessment Activity 1 (continued)

★ PROCEDURES

1. Review the background information about North American civilizations between 3000 B.C. and the A.D. 1500s.

2. Select the civilizations that you will be including on your map. Determine the location of each civilization and whether each civilization was based on a hunting economy, a farming economy, or a combination of both hunting and farming. For each civilization, research as much economic and cultural information as possible. Summarize your research on the lines below.

_____

_____

_____

_____

_____

_____

_____

_____

3. Study various maps to discover how legends can be used to show information.

4. Design a legend that will convey the information you want to present. The legend may use colors and symbols to highlight your information. Create your map's legend on the lines below.

_____

_____

_____

5. On a large piece of paper, draw or trace an outline of North America. Fill in the outline by marking the boundaries of each civilization you have chosen. Label each area with the name of the appropriate civilization. Add the information in your legend.

6. Give your map to several classmates to critique.

7. From your classmates' comments, revise your map and legend for clarity.

8. Be prepared to discuss your map with your classmates.

★ ASSESSMENT

1. Use the Assessment Lists suggested to evaluate your map.

2. Check to see that you have included all elements; improve as needed.

3. Complete a final self-assessment of your work before you share it.

The American Vision

★ Performance Assessment Activity 2

Use with Chapter 2

The Jamestown Settlement

★ BACKGROUND

In 1604 a group of English businesspeople asked the king of England, James I, for permission to start colonies in Virginia. James I agreed to their request, and these investors became known as the Virginia Company. In 1606 the Virginia Company sent three small ships and 144 men to Virginia. After a very difficult journey, the colonists founded a settlement that they named Jamestown. From the beginning, the Jamestown colonists experienced problems. The site they chose for their town was a breeding ground for malaria-carrying mosquitoes. Few of the colonists could fish or hunt, and none of the original colonists knew how to raise livestock or cultivate crops. The colonists who came from the English upper classes refused to do manual labor. Arguing and bickering among the settlers became common. By 1608 most of the original colonists had died because of lawlessness, sickness, and food shortages.

In 1609, 400 new settlers arrived in Jamestown. However, the winter of 1609–1610 was very difficult. By the spring of 1610, only 60 settlers were still alive. The governor of the colony and his deputy drafted a harsh code of laws that helped to organize the colonists. The colonists began to harvest tobacco, and the money received from tobacco sales and the promise of free land helped to attract more settlers to the new world. By 1622 more than 4,500 settlers had arrived in Virginia. This alarmed the Native Americans, who attacked Jamestown. The colony was devastated. The English court blamed the Virginia Company for the 350 deaths in the colony, and the company's charter was revoked. Virginia became a royal colony run by a governor who was appointed by the king.

★ TASK

You are a tour guide in Jamestown and you give an oral presentation describing the events that led to the settlement of Jamestown, the difficulties the settlers faced, and the results of the Native American uprising of 1622. The events in your presentation should be given in chronological order.

★ AUDIENCE

Visitors to Jamestown are your intended audience.

★ PURPOSE

The purpose of this activity is to create an oral presentation that will give visitors to Jamestown accurate historical background about the colony. Your research will allow visitors to analyze the successes and failures of the Jamestown settlement.

★ Performance Assessment Activity 2 (continued)

✦ PROCEDURES

1. Determine the religious, economic, and political changes in England that caused the English to establish colonies along the eastern coast of North America. Summarize your research on the following lines.

_____

_____

_____

_____

2. Research the events surrounding the arrival of the first settlers at Jamestown. Include information concerning the 1606 voyage to Virginia, the problems the early settlers encountered, and the events of the winter of 1609–1610. Use the lines below to organize your information.

_____

_____

_____

_____

3. Research the impact of tobacco on the economy of the Jamestown settlement and how this contributed to new immigration to the colony. Include information on how this immigration led to the devastation of Jamestown. Write notes on the lines below.

_____

_____

_____

_____

4. Use the lines below to prepare an outline for your report.

_____

_____

_____

_____

5. Present your talk to some friends and listen to their reactions. Based on your friends' comments, make any necessary adjustments to your talk.

6. Give your oral presentation.

✦ ASSESSMENT

1. Use the Assessment Lists suggested to evaluate your oral presentation.

2. Check to see that you have included all elements; improve as needed.

3. Complete a final self-assessment of your work before you share it.

★ Performance Assessment Activity 3

Use with Chapter 3

Colonial Life

✭ BACKGROUND

In the 1700s, changes were taking place in Europe that greatly affected American society. One cultural movement, the Enlightenment, stressed solving problems through reason instead of relying on the church. This was also known as rationalism. Another movement, the Great Awakening, stressed praying and an emotional union with God. This view became popular among farmers, workers, and slaves. During this time, the population of the American colonies was growing rapidly. On average, a colonial woman gave birth to seven children, but it was not uncommon for some women to have as many as fourteen children. The legal status of women continued to improve. Although there were still legal limitations to what women could do, many colonial women operated businesses. People were also living longer because of improved housing, better sanitation, and advances in medicine. Many immigrants arrived in the colonies during this period as well. German immigrants, who were interested in religious freedom, settled in Pennsylvania. The Scotch-Irish came to America to escape rising taxes, poor harvests, and religious discrimination. Jews arrived in New Amsterdam and later moved throughout the colonies. They, too, were seeking an opportunity to practice their religion. However, there were also many unwilling immigrants to the colonies. These were enslaved Africans who had been forcibly brought to America. Most of these Africans lived on plantations in the Southern Colonies, where they were made to work for the plantation owners. Many Africans developed ways to fight back against slavery. Some resisted by running away or by using passive resistance. Others banded together to attack overseers.

✭ TASK

You have been asked by a publishing company to create a chart for a history book that will be read by high school students. The subject of the chart is colonial life in the 1700s. Your chart will include written information and visuals under the headings of Family Life, Immigrants, Africans, and Cultural Movements. Under each heading, you will include information on the economic, cultural, and social factors that contributed to life in colonial America. You will also include visual elements to make your chart more appealing. Visuals may include drawings or graphs. You will present your chart on poster board.

✭ AUDIENCE

Your audience is high school students.

✭ PURPOSE

The purpose of this activity is to give you experience in organizing information in chart form and to summarize the issues affecting colonial life in the 1700s.

★ Performance Assessment Activity 3 (continued)

✪ PROCEDURES

1. Review the background information concerning colonial life in the 1700s.

2. Make an outline for your chart on the lines below. Include the heads and sub-heads you will use. Clarifying the subheads will allow you to do further research.

_____

_____

_____

_____

_____

_____

_____

3. Conduct research to discover as many facts as possible to include under your subheads.

4. Organize your information under four headings—Family Life, Immigrants, Africans, and Cultural Movements—and write a rough draft of the information that will appear in your chart.

5. Create a title for your chart and record it on the following line.

_____

6. Look at other charts and posters and make notes on ideas that can add interest to your chart, such as using drawings, color, or graphic elements. Make notes on the lines below.

_____

_____

_____

_____

7. Make a rough sketch of the chart, and indicate the visual elements you will include. You may want to make photocopies of illustrations you find in your sources to cut out and use, or you may want to make your own illustrations.

8. Exchange your draft and rough sketch with a partner for comments and suggestions.

9. Make any changes you think are necessary, and make your final chart on poster board.

✪ ASSESSMENT

1. Use the Assessment Lists suggested to evaluate your chart.

2. Check to see that you have included all elements; improve as needed.

3. Complete a final self-assessment of your work before you share it.

The American Vision

★ Performance Assessment Activity 4

Use with Chapter 4

Diary of a Patriot

★ BACKGROUND

Tensions between Great Britain and its American colonies grew as British leaders sought greater control over their North American empire. Earlier, in the 1740s, both the British and the French became interested in the Ohio River Valley. The French attacked and seized a fort that was being built by the British in western Pennsylvania. The governor of Virginia, Robert Dinwiddie, asked George Washington, a young officer in the Virginia militia, to raise a force and expel the French in 1754. Although Washington was not successful in his attempt to regain the fort, he continued to be a major participant in the struggles of the young republic. As a member of Virginia's House of Burgesses, Washington participated in the convention that passed the non-importation agreement, which blocked the sale of British goods in Virginia. In 1775 the Second Continental Congress set up the Continental Army and appointed Washington as its general. Washington's troops, although they were more inexperienced than the British troops, participated in the defense of New York City and the Battle of White Plains. In December 1776, Washington and his men crossed the Delaware River from Pennsylvania to New Jersey and won victories against Hessian mercenaries at Trenton and British regiments at Princeton. In 1777 Washington's troops were defeated at the Battle of Brandywine Creek. In October 1781, Washington's aide, Alexander Hamilton, led an attack that captured the British defenses at Yorktown, where the British surrendered.

★ TASK

You are keeping a diary on George Washington's actions between the years 1754–1781. Your plan is to write a book someday about George Washington and his participation in the events leading up to the British surrender at Yorktown. Write diary entries for 10 important days during the American Revolution. Your diary will include the names of any committees or organizations George Washington belonged to, the military campaigns fought or led by Washington, and the role he played in each battle.

★ AUDIENCE

The future readers of your book are your intended audience.

★ PURPOSE

The purpose of your diary is to chronicle detailed notes about George Washington's actions during the events leading up to the American Revolution and during the American Revolution itself. You will use your diary as the basis for writing a book about George Washington and the American Revolution.

★ Performance Assessment Activity 4 (continued)

✪ PROCEDURES

1. Review information on the events leading up to the American Revolution.

2. Research to learn more about George Washington. Include the names of organizations he belonged to and events that he participated in during the years leading up to the American Revolution. On the lines below, write several facts about George Washington's life that you can include in your diary.

_____

_____

3. Research to learn more about the circumstances surrounding some of the military campaigns George Washington either fought in or led. Include military losses as well as victories. Make notes on some of the physical hardships Washington encountered in leading his men. Find a way to include these notes in your diary entries. Summarize your research on the lines below.

_____

_____

4. Research how the writings of Thomas Paine influenced Washington. Include quotes from Paine's *Common Sense* or *The American Crisis* in your diary entries.

5. Choose 10 important events or dates on which you will make your diary entries and list them chronologically on the following lines.

_____

_____

_____

_____

_____

_____

_____

_____

_____

6. Write a diary entry for each date listed. Include your own reactions to these events and make personal observations about George Washington.

7. Give a draft of your diary to a classmate for comments and suggestions.

8. Write your diary, including any revisions that will improve your work.

✪ ASSESSMENT

1. Use the Assessment Lists suggested to evaluate your diary entries.

2. Check to see that you have included all elements; improve as needed.

3. Complete a final self-assessment of your work before you share it.

★ Performance Assessment Activity 5

Use with Chapter 5

A New Constitution

★ BACKGROUND

The delegates to the Philadelphia Convention in 1787 met to revise the Articles of Confederation. Instead, they ended up framing a new form of government in the Constitution of the United States. The process, however, was not a smooth one. The delegates did not always have the same goals and interests, and tempers often flared. Some delegates proposed scrapping the Articles of Confederation. Others wanted to keep the Articles of Confederation but modify them to make the central government stronger. Delegates from the smaller states demanded changes that would protect them against the voting power of the larger states. The Northern and Southern states were divided over how to treat slavery in the new constitution. Some delegates feared that a strong national government with the power to regulate trade might impose taxes on exports or ban imports from other countries. The only way for the delegates to resolve these issues was to honestly debate their differences and find some middle ground.

★ TASK

You are going to participate in a roundtable discussion with six people. During the roundtable discussion, each student will assume the role of a person who attended the Constitutional Convention. Your role may be that of one of the leaders of the Convention, or you may choose to represent a lawyer, planter, or merchant. A moderator will ask each member of the roundtable his or her opinion about issues such as voting rights, taxation, and slavery. Each student will research information about his or her role and present that information during the discussion.

★ AUDIENCE

Your group will conduct your roundtable discussion for other students in your class. Other students from your school may also be asked to attend the discussion.

★ PURPOSE

The purpose of this roundtable discussion is to provide experience in participating in moderated discussions and to present a political viewpoint by portraying one of the Framers of the Constitution.

★ PROCEDURES

1. The class will be organized into discussion groups of approximately six students each. Each student should decide on a role to portray. Write the name or profession of the delegate you have chosen to portray on the line below.

_____

★ Performance Assessment Activity 5 (continued)

2. Individually, review information on the positions taken by your delegate. Do further research on your delegate's contribution to the convention. To help give you ideas about your delegate, look for personal accounts and other historical information in the library.

3. Use the lines below to organize your information. Include your character's feelings about government, slavery, taxation, the British government, and local government. Include any other relevant issues.

_____

_____

_____

_____

_____

_____

4. Discuss the information you have gathered with your group. If necessary, revise the issues you will discuss during your roundtable. Describe your issues on the lines below.

_____

_____

_____

_____

5. Choose a moderator, and plan how the moderator will introduce each member of the roundtable and the order of the issues you will discuss.

6. Practice your roundtable discussion with your group. Make sure that the gathered facts are presented during the discussion and that your audience will understand the different viewpoints your group represents.

7. Present your roundtable discussion. Use name cards so that your audience knows each speaker. Your cards may include a label such as "Merchant" or "Lawyer," or the card may contain the name of an actual delegate.

8. As a class, critique each discussion. Talk about the new information you learned, and how the discussion was presented. After all of the roundtables have been presented, you may want to hold an informal discussion among delegates from different areas. For example, you may want to hold a discussion between a delegate from New Jersey and a delegate from New York or a discussion between a merchant and a planter.

★ ASSESSMENT

1. Use the Assessment Lists suggested to evaluate your roundtable discussion.

2. Check to see that you have included all elements; improve as needed.

3. Complete a final self-assessment of your work before you share it.

The American Vision

★ Performance Assessment Activity 6

Use with Chapter 6

The Lewis and Clark Expedition

✪ BACKGROUND

After his election, Thomas Jefferson set a new style for the presidency. Jefferson believed that George Washington and John Adams had acted too much like royalty, and he tried to create a less formal style. Jefferson rode horseback instead of traveling in carriages, and he preferred to entertain at intimate dinners around a circular table instead of having formal receptions. Jefferson, who was a strong supporter of states' rights, hoped to limit the scope of the federal government. He began paying off the government debt, and he cut government spending. Jefferson did away with all excise taxes and, instead of a standing army, he planned to rely on local militia. One of Jefferson's strongest beliefs was that a republic could only survive if most of the people were farmers who owned their own land. This belief led him to support the idea of expanding the country farther west.

In 1803 the United States bought Louisiana from France. Even before Louisiana became a part of the United States, though, Jefferson asked Congress to fund a secret expedition into the Louisiana Territory to trace the Missouri River and find a route to the Pacific Ocean. After Congress approved the expedition, Jefferson chose Meriwether Lewis and William Clark to lead it. In 1804 the expedition headed west. Along the way they met Sacagawea, a Shoshone woman who joined the expedition as a guide and interpreter. The expedition found a path through the Rocky Mountains and eventually traced the Columbia River to the Pacific Ocean. The expedition not only greatly increased American knowledge of the Louisiana Territory, but it also gave the United States a claim to the Oregon Territory along the coast.

✪ TASK

You are going to write a magazine article on the Lewis and Clark expedition. Your article should discuss the purpose of the expedition, the members of the expedition, the route the expedition took, interesting facts concerning the expedition, and the results of the expedition. Your article will be published in a history magazine.

✪ AUDIENCE

Your audience is readers of the magazine.

✪ PURPOSE

The purpose of this activity is to inform readers about the Lewis and Clark expedition and to create an article worthy of publication.

✪ PROCEDURES

1. Gather information on the Lewis and Clark expedition. Consult as many different resources as you can. You may look for personal accounts and other historical information in the library. Include as much information as possible on Sacagawea and her role in the expedition.

★ Performance Assessment Activity 6 (continued)

2. Make an outline of your article on the lines below. Your article should begin by briefly describing the purpose of the Lewis and Clark expedition.

_____

_____

_____

_____

_____

_____

_____

_____

_____

_____

_____

_____

3. Write a title for your article on the line below.

_____

4. Find and make a photocopy of a piece of art that relates to your article. Write a caption for the illustration on the lines below.

_____

_____

_____

5. Write a rough draft of your article.

6. Give your article to a classmate for comments and suggestions. Ask your class-mate if any part of the article is unclear.

7. Write your final article after making any necessary revisions.

■ ASSESSMENT

1. Use the Assessment Lists suggested to evaluate your magazine article.

2. Check to see that you have included all elements; improve as needed.

3. Complete a final self-assessment of your work before you share it.

★ Performance Assessment Activity 7

Use with Chapter 7

Life in the South

★ BACKGROUND

Southern society was largely based on agriculture and the practice of slavery. In areas throughout the South, farmers grew tobacco and sugarcane, and rice was grown in the coastal regions. No crop, however, was more widely grown than cotton. After the invention of the cotton gin, Southern farmers were able to produce large amounts of cotton to sell to textile mills in Europe. With better methods of producing cotton and the ready markets in England, the demand for slave labor skyrocketed.

The agricultural economy shaped Southern life and produced a well-defined social structure for the region. The planters, who owned the region's larger plantations and were slaveholders, were at the top of society. Planters were those farmers who held 20 or more enslaved people. Although they were relatively few in number, planters were often very wealthy, and they dominated the region's economy and political and legal systems. Ordinary farmers, called yeoman farmers, and their families made up the vast majority of the white population. Some yeomen owned as many as four enslaved persons. Close to the bottom of the social ladder were the rural poor. Most of this group were illiterate and lived by hunting and fishing, vegetable gardening, and raising a few hogs and chickens. At the bottom of society were African Americans, who made up nearly 37 percent of the total Southern population. Approximately 93 percent of all African Americans were enslaved. In addition, there was a small urban class of lawyers, doctors, and other professionals. The influence of agriculture was so great, though, that most of the members of this class also owned farms or invested in farming.

★ TASK

You are a writer for a Northern newspaper. Your editor has asked you to write an in-depth article on agriculture and its influence on social structure in the South. You will include information concerning the planters, yeoman farmers, the rural poor, African Americans, and the urban class in your article.

★ AUDIENCE

The readers of the newspaper are your intended audience.

★ PURPOSE

The purpose of this activity is to give you experience in writing for a newspaper. You will also educate your readers about the classes in Southern society and the role of agriculture in that society.

★ PROCEDURES

1. Review the background information concerning agriculture in the South. Find data concerning which crops were grown and harvested in various locations and where these crops were marketed. Research King Cotton and the role it played in creating the Southern social structure. Include information concerning the invention of the cotton gin.

★ Performance Assessment Activity 7 (continued)

2. Use as many sources as possible to research information concerning the planters and yeoman farmers. Include data concerning which class was more prosperous, which had the greater number of members, and the approximate number of slaveholders in each. Summarize your research on the lines below.

_____

_____

_____

_____

_____

_____

3. Use as many sources as possible to gather data concerning the rural poor, African Americans, and the urban class. Include data concerning literacy rates, approximate number of people in each class, and the relative wealth of the members of these classes. Make notes on the lines below.

_____

_____

_____

_____

_____

_____

4. Create a headline for your article. The headline must grab the attention of your readers and reflect the content of the article. Write your headline on the line below.

_____

5. Write a rough draft of your article. Remember that you are trying to educate Northern readers about Southern society.

6. Exchange your rough draft with a classmate for a peer review. Ask your classmate for feedback concerning article content and clarity.

7. Write your final newspaper article after making any necessary revisions.

★ ASSESSMENT

1. Use the Assessment Lists suggested to evaluate your newspaper article.

2. Check to see that you have included all elements; improve as needed.

3. Complete a final self-assessment of your work before you share it.

The American Vision

★ Performance Assessment Activity 8

Use with Chapter 8

Andrew Jackson for President!

★ BACKGROUND

Beginning in the 1800s, the nation witnessed a growth of democracy. Government became more inclusive, and ordinary citizens became a greater force in the political arena. After many states lowered or eliminated property ownership as a voting quali-fication, many new voters were able to cast ballots in presidential elections. Some of the citizens who voted for the first time in the 1828 presidential election helped Andrew Jackson win his first term as president. Jackson believed that the majority should rule in a democracy and that ordinary citizens should play a prominent role in government. He made the electoral system more open by replacing the caucus sys-tem with a nominating convention. He also used the spoils system—the practice of appointing people to government jobs on the basis of party loyalty and support. During Jackson's first term in office, he defended the Union when the Nullification Crisis threatened to divide the nation further. However, Jackson's wish to expand democracy did not extend to everyone. Jackson did not believe that women, African Americans, or Native Americans should be given the right to vote. In fact, in 1830 Jackson signed the Indian Removal Act, which gave money and support to states to relocate Native Americans. Most Native Americans eventually decided to give in to state pressure and resettled in the West, but the army was called in to move the Cherokee out of Georgia. Because of the hardships the Native Americans suffered, this journey became known as the "Trail of Tears." Jackson, who was a slaveholder, ignored the slavery issue. He did, however, oppose the National Bank. When Congress passed a bill to extend the Bank's charter for an additional 20 years, Jackson vetoed the bill. In 1832 the Democrats held a convention to renominate Andrew Jackson for president.

★ TASK

You are Andrew Jackson's campaign manager for the 1832 presidential election. You are going to compose a memorandum to Jackson to offer suggestions on running his political campaign. Your memo will offer details on strategies that could be used to win the election. It will include personal details about Jackson that you believe will appeal to voters. The memo will include points that the candidate should make about issues of the day, such as the National Bank and slavery, and how to refute the oppo-nent's positions. Your memo may also suggest how Jackson might characterize him-self in order to win the continued confidence of the voters.

★ AUDIENCE

Although the memo is intended for Andrew Jackson, the members of your class are your audience.

★ Performance Assessment Activity 8 (continued)

✦ PURPOSE

The purpose of this activity is to highlight the issues presented in a political campaign and to display the tactics politicians might use to win presidential campaigns. It will also give you practice in composing a memo.

✦ PROCEDURES

1. Review information on the election of 1828 and, particularly, the election of 1832. Research the main political issues of the 1832 campaign. Record the position that Jackson took on each of these issues. Make notes on the lines below.

_____

_____

_____

2. List the crises of Jackson's first term in office and how Jackson handled those issues. Determine how Jackson will rebut any criticisms of how he handled those crises. Record your notes on the lines below.

_____

_____

_____

3. Investigate the role of a campaign manager. Make a few notes on the role of a campaign manager on the lines below.

_____

_____

4. Write a catchy phrase to use as the subject of your memo.

_____

5. Make an outline of your memo, including headings to indicate a change of subject. Organize information under your headings. Write your outline on the lines below.

_____

_____

_____

6. Write a rough draft of your memo. The tone of the memo should be familiar, yet respectful. You are a friend of Andrew Jackson.

7. Exchange your memo with a classmate for a peer review.

8. Write your memo, including the necessary revisions.

✦ ASSESSMENT

1. Use the Assessment Lists suggested to evaluate your memorandum.

2. Check to see that you have included all elements; improve as needed.

3. Complete a final self-assessment of your work before you share it.

★ Performance Assessment Activity 9

Use with Chapter 9

Let's Go!

★ BACKGROUND

Americans first began heading west in the early 1800s. By 1850 over 4 million settlers had crossed the Mississippi River and marked out farms on the richest land they could find. These pioneers were called squatters, because they settled on land that they did not own. Life for pioneers was hard, and most of the pioneer families struggled as they worked their small farms. Farmers cooperated to clear land, raise barns, and harvest crops. As more farmers began to settle in the Midwest, people began looking toward California and Oregon. Most emigrants assumed that the Great Plains contained poor land for farming, so they were eager to get to the richer farmlands in the far West. However, other nations, as well as some Native American groups, had already laid claim to parts of Oregon and California.

Travelers needed to cross nearly 2,000 miles to get to the Pacific Coast. Although the Oregon Trail was the most popular trail through the Great Plains, some emigrants used the California Trail or the Santa Fe Trail. The journey, which was usually made in covered wagons, was extremely difficult. Supplies were often scarce, bad weather presented problems, and often the trails were not well marked. There were sometimes attacks by Plains Indians, who feared that the increasing flow of emigrants across their hunting grounds would disrupt the buffalo herds. In 1851 the federal government negotiated the Treaty of Fort Laramie with the Plains Indians. According to this treaty, eight Native American groups agreed to stay within specific geographic boundaries, and the United States promised that these defined territories would belong to the Native Americans forever.

★ TASK

You and your family work a small farm on the banks of the Mississippi River. You believe that there are better opportunities for your family in California. You are going to prepare a persuasive argument to convince your family to move west. You will organize your ideas on paper and then read them aloud to your family.

★ AUDIENCE

Your family and the members of your class are your audience.

★ PURPOSE

The purpose of this activity is to create a written, persuasive argument.

★ PROCEDURES

1. Research the westward movement of emigrants in the mid-1800s. Your information should include why people chose to move to the Pacific coast and the routes these emigrants took. Gather information concerning the hardships of travel in covered wagons, problems presented by the weather, the scarcity of supplies, and the frequency of Native American attacks. Include any information you can find concerning federal treaties with various Native American groups.

★ Performance Assessment Activity 9 (continued)

2. Decide which route you think would be best for your family to take to California. Determine where the route begins and ends, and whether it is possible to travel with a guide. Determine points of interest that lie on the route and use these in your argument to your family. Make notes on the lines below.

_____

_____

_____

_____

_____

3. Make a list of the advantages that you believe await your family in California. Make a few notes on the following lines.

_____

_____

_____

_____

4. List the objections or worries your family might have in undertaking this journey. Beside each objection, make a note of how you intend to respond to your family's concerns. Make notes on the lines below.

_____

_____

_____

_____

_____

_____

5. Make a draft of your argument, using language and reasoning that will appeal to your family. Remember that your argument will be read aloud.

6. Give your draft to a classmate for comments and suggestions.

7. Write the final draft of your persuasive argument, incorporating any necessary revisions.

8. Present your persuasive argument to your classmates.

★ ASSESSMENT

1. Use the Assessment Lists suggested to evaluate your persuasive argument.

2. Check to see that you have included all elements; improve as needed.

3. Complete a final self-assessment of your work before you share it.

★ Performance Assessment Activity 10

Use with Chapter 10

Slave State or Free?

★ BACKGROUND

By 1850 tension between the North and the South had increased dramatically. As new land was acquired, the debate over whether these new states should be slave states or free states further divided public opinion. The Mexican-American War had opened new land to American settlers. The Wilmot Proviso, which proposed that the new territories should be free territories, made many people angry. Some people believed that the citizens of each state should be allowed to vote to determine for themselves whether they wanted to permit slavery. The members of the Free-Soil Party opposed the spread of slavery into the new states because they believed that slavery would make it difficult for free men to find work.

In 1849 gold was discovered in California. Nearly 80,000 people rushed to California, hoping to strike it rich. A strong government was needed to ensure people's safety, so California began to prepare itself for statehood. In 1849 California applied for admission as a free state. However, if California entered the union as a free state, the slaveholding states would become a minority in the Senate. Some Southern politicians began to talk about secession. An influential senator from Kentucky, Henry Clay, offered a series of proposals to solve the slavery crisis and ease the tension between the North and the South. These proposals, which were grouped in pairs, caused yet another debate in Congress. Senator Calhoun, who was an advocate of the South's rights, believed that Clay's compromise would not save the Union. Calhoun believed that the South's rights to slavery needed to be preserved, even if those rights were preserved by secession. Eventually, Clay's proposal was divided into several smaller bills. This allowed members of Congress to vote for the parts of the bill that they wanted and abstain from voting on other issues. By the fall of 1850, all of the parts of Clay's original bill had been passed by Congress and signed into law by President Fillmore. This became known as the Compromise of 1850.

★ TASK

You are going to take a position on whether the new states that are admitted to the Union should be slaveholding states or free states and write a political pamphlet that supports your point of view. Your pamphlet will contain the proposals put forth in the Compromise of 1850 and give reasons citizens should either accept or reject those proposals. You will also include any other topics that you feel will support your position either for or against the Compromise of 1850.

★ AUDIENCE

Your fellow citizens are your intended audience.

★ Performance Assessment Activity 10 (continued)

★ PURPOSE

The purpose of this activity is for you to gain experience in writing a political pamphlet. You will take a position on issues surrounding the Compromise of 1850 and advocate your cause.

★ PROCEDURES

1. Review the background information on the issues leading up to the Compromise of 1850. Discuss these issues with your class and with your teacher. Use the following lines to list as many issues as you can surrounding the slavery/free state issues of the 1850s.

   _____

   _____

   _____

   _____

   _____

2. Decide the position you will take on each issue. Research information on each position you decide to advocate. Make notes on the lines below.

   _____

   _____

   _____

   _____

   _____

3. Research examples of pamphlets or political letters from the 1850s. You may want to imitate the language in use at the time, or you may want to use contemporary language to convey your ideas.

4. Write a draft of your pamphlet. Your pamphlet should be approximately two pages long and include titles and subheads. Design your pamphlet so that it will attract attention. Create an eye-catching title for your pamphlet. Write the title on the line below.

   _____

5. Write your political pamphlet. Be sure that it supports your cause. Consider how you can persuade people to adopt your position.

6. Present your pamphlet to a classmate. With your classmate, critique the pamphlet for clarity and the excitement that it creates for your cause.

★ ASSESSMENT

1. Use the Assessment Lists suggested to evaluate your political pamphlet.

2. Check to see that you have included all elements; improve as needed.

3. Complete a final self-assessment of your work before you share it.

The American Vision

★ Performance Assessment Activity 11

Use with Chapter 11

Lee or Grant?

★ BACKGROUND

In the spring of 1864, the most successful general of the Union army—Ulysses S. Grant—faced the most renowned Confederate commander—Robert E. Lee. Both men had fought many hard battles and commanded many campaigns. Although he had originally been asked by President Lincoln to command the Union army, Lee turned him down to fight for the South. Lee had been born in the South, and he felt that he could not fight against the land of his birth. Lee, who was a daring and forceful leader, met and defeated Union troops in several significant battles, including Fredericksburg and Chancellorsville. He favored invading the North to secure a Southern victory. Grant, who fought for the Union, also won many battles, including decisive victories at Chattanooga and Vicksburg. Grant was eventually promoted to lieutenant general, a rank that no one had held since George Washington. Finally, at Appomattox Courthouse on April 9, 1865, Lee was forced to surrender to Grant. Grant offered generous terms of surrender to Lee. Grant agreed to let Confederates take their horses home in order to help with planting crops for the winter, and he agreed not to prosecute Confederate soldiers for treason.

★ TASK

You have been asked to give a lecture to a group of cadets at a military academy. The head of the academy wants you to choose either Lee or Grant as the subject of your lecture. Although you will include as much biographical information as possible on your choice, the focus of your lecture will be on battles and military tactics during the Civil War.

★ AUDIENCE

The cadets attending your lecture are your audience.

★ PURPOSE

The purpose of this activity is to give you experience in giving a lecture. You will gather facts and present them in an orderly, logical manner to your audience. Your lecture should contribute to your audience's greater understanding of the leaders and battles of the Civil War.

★ PROCEDURES

1. Review the background information concerning the Civil War. Decide whether the topic of your lecture will be Robert E. Lee or Ulysses S. Grant. Find as much information as you can concerning the early life of the man you select. Write the name of the man and any biographical data you can find on the following lines.

_____

_____

★ **Performance Assessment Activity 11** (continued)

2. List the economic advantages and disadvantages your subject faced in his attempts to win the war. Indicate the military tactics and technologies that were available to your subject. Use the following lines for your notes.

_____

_____

_____

3. List the major battles or military campaigns your subject fought or led, the intended goals of those battles and campaigns, and whether your subject won or lost each one. Make notes on the following lines.

_____

_____

_____

4. Research the events at Appomattox. Facts from that battle and its aftermath will be used as the conclusion of your lecture. Make notes on the lines below.

_____

_____

_____

5. Use the lines below to prepare an outline for your lecture.

_____

_____

_____

_____

_____

6. Present your lecture to some friends and listen to their reactions. Based on your friends' comments, make any necessary adjustments to your lecture.

7. Give your lecture. Submit your notes and outline to your teacher.

✪ **ASSESSMENT**

1. Use the Assessment Lists suggested to evaluate your lecture.

2. Check to see that you have included all elements; improve as needed.

3. Complete a final self-assessment of your work before you share it.

★ **Performance Assessment Activity 12**

Use with Chapter 12

A Look at Reconstruction

★ BACKGROUND

By the end of the Civil War, the economy of the South had been destroyed, and thousands of people were unemployed, homeless, and hungry. Roads, bridges, and railroad tracks had been demolished, and cities had been looted and burned. Because enslaved African Americans had been emancipated, the agricultural system—which had relied upon slave labor—failed. Many of the freed African Americans followed Union troops as they marched through the South because there was no place for these freedmen to go. People in the North disagreed on how to rebuild the South. Lincoln, for example, believed that it was the responsibility of the president to direct Reconstruction. He believed that a moderate policy would work best, and he wanted to offer amnesty or pardon to all Southerners who were allowed to take an oath of loyalty to the United States. The Radical Republicans, on the other hand, thought that Reconstruction should be handled by Congress. They did not want to reconcile with the South. The Radical Republicans wanted to completely redo the systems that the South had relied upon prior to the Civil War. There was also disagreement on support for equality and rights for African Americans. Moderates thought that Lincoln was being too lenient, but they also thought that the Radical Republicans were showing too much support for African Americans. People had to decide under what terms and conditions the former Confederate states would rejoin the Union and what rights would be extended to African Americans. Eventually, laws were passed that determined how Reconstruction would be handled. Some of the laws dealt with education and employment for former slaves. Other laws became amendments to the Constitution.

★ TASK

Although you live in the North, you are very interested in the issues surrounding Reconstruction. You are going to write a three-page letter to a friend who lives in Great Britain. In your letter, you will outline the problems faced by the South, how the president and Congress believe that Reconstruction should be handled, and the special problems faced by African Americans. Your letter will include codes that have been established, federal agencies that have been formed, and laws that have been passed to assist Reconstruction efforts.

★ AUDIENCE

Your audience is the recipient of your letter.

★ PURPOSE

The purpose of this activity is to give you experience in letter writing. In your letter, you will also illustrate your depth of knowledge concerning the issues surrounding Southern Reconstruction.

★ Performance Assessment Activity 12 (continued)

★ PROCEDURES

1. Review information concerning Reconstruction.

2. Make notes on how Lincoln's plan for Reconstruction differed from that of the Radical Republicans. Write your notes on the following lines.

_____

_____

_____

_____

3. Name a federal agency that was formed to help with the refugee crisis, and list the tasks undertaken by that federal agency. Use the following lines for your notes.

_____

_____

_____

4. List codes and laws that were established to assist Reconstruction. Write a short summary of the content of each law. Make notes on the following lines.

_____

_____

_____

_____

5. Make notes on your personal beliefs concerning Reconstruction. Include your thoughts on rights you believe should be extended to African Americans. Summarize your thoughts on the following lines.

_____

_____

_____

6. Recall that the format for writing a letter includes a date, greeting, body, and closing.

7. Write a draft of your letter.

8. Give your letter to one of your classmates for peer review.

9. Revise your letter by clarifying details and using descriptive writing that will interest your reader.

★ ASSESSMENT

1. Use the Assessment Lists suggested to evaluate your letter.

2. Check to see that you have included all elements; improve as needed.

3. Complete a final self-assessment of your work before you share it.

The American Vision

★ Performance Assessment Activity 13

Use with Chapter 13

Heading West

✖ BACKGROUND

During the years from 1865 to 1900, many events were taking place throughout the Great Plains and the West. A large silver strike in Nevada and the discovery of gold and silver in Colorado brought many West in search of riches. Railroads provided quick and reliable transportation to settlers whose previous mode of transportation had usually been by wagon train. Ranching became a big business, and cattle drives allowed ranchers to sell to new markets. Settlers began staking out homesteads on the Great Plains. Wheat became an important crop. By the 1890s, though, the large amount of wheat on the market caused wheat prices to drop. The weather cycle changed, and many farmers struggled to survive.

The Native Americans, who had lived on the Great Plains for years, found that the settlers and the people crossing the Great Plains to get to the West were taking a toll on the hunting grounds. The Dakota and Lakota Sioux fought to defend their territories and their way of life. Native American leaders such as Red Cloud, Crazy Horse, and Sitting Bull led forays against government troops. In 1864 Colonel John Chivington killed several hundred Native American men, women, and children in what became known as the Sand Creek Massacre. In 1876 Lieutenant Colonel George Armstrong Custer and his troops were defeated at the Battle of Little Bighorn. In 1890 a fierce battle ensued at Wounded Knee, and 200 Lakota Sioux lost their lives. Congress passed the Dawes Act in 1887. This act provided land to Native Americans so that they could farm and eventually be absorbed into American society as landowners and citizens. The plan failed to achieve its goals.

✖ TASK

You are going to choose a book that focuses on events in the Great Plains or the West from 1865 to 1900 and write a book review. Choose a topic of interest to you. You will read the book, write a review of the book, and place the events in the book in historical context. You will also give your opinion about the book's factual accuracy and reliability.

✖ AUDIENCE

The members of your class are your intended audience.

✖ PURPOSE

The purpose of this activity is to give you experience in writing a book review. You will also gain a deeper understanding of the Great Plains and the West during the late 1800s.

✖ PROCEDURES

1. Review information about the Great Plains and the West from 1865 to 1900. Choose a topic of particular interest to you. Your topic may be mining, cattle

★ Performance Assessment Activity 13 (continued)

ranching, settlers of the Great Plains, Native Americans, military campaigns against the Native Americans, or any other topic you prefer. Write your topic on the line below.

_____

2. Find a book to read and review. You may use one of the books mentioned in your textbook, or you may find a book in the library. Write the title and author of your book on the following line.

_____

3. In your review, you will include events that occur in the book and place those events in historical context. Use the following lines to make notes on significant events in your book.

_____

_____

_____

_____

_____

_____

_____

_____

_____

_____

4. In your review, include your own opinion as to whether the events that take place in the book are fact or historical fiction. Cite passages in the book that bolster your opinion. Make notes on the following lines.

_____

_____

_____

_____

5. Organize your information and write a draft of your book review. Be sure to include the book title and author on the first page of the review.

6. Exchange drafts with a classmate for peer review.

7. Make revisions as necessary and write your final book review.

★ ASSESSMENT

1. Use the Assessment Lists suggested to evaluate your book review.

2. Check to see that you have included all elements; improve as needed.

3. Complete a final self-assessment of your work before you share it.

★ Performance Assessment Activity 14

Use with Chapter 14

Strike!

★ BACKGROUND

In the late 1800s, industrial workers were plagued with many problems. Wages were low, and people were often forced to work long hours in unhealthy and dangerous conditions. Workers were threatened by pay cuts or layoffs. All of these factors contributed to a rise in the number of labor unions. Labor unions faced strong opposition from employers, who used tactics such as blacklists, lockouts, and strikebreakers to retaliate against union organizing. Law enforcement usually supported employers against unions, and the police would sometimes use force to break up strikes. Despite these challenges, new unions arose. Among these new unions were the National Labor Union, the Noble Order of the Knights of Labor, and the American Federation of Labor. The National Labor Union had 640,000 members that included representatives of farmers groups, the woman suffrage movement, and other reformers. The Knights of Labor, which accepted both skilled and unskilled laborers, had a membership of 700,000 workers in 1885, but membership declined after the Haymarket Square riot in Chicago. As membership in the Knights of Labor began to diminish, the American Federation of Labor was organized. The American Federation of Labor, led by Samuel Gompers, accepted only skilled workers, and it organized those workers into separate unions. Each union was devoted to a different craft. Most women were unable to join the American Federation of Labor because women were classified as unskilled workers. New unions rose to represent women. Mary Kennedy O'Sullivan and Leonora O'Reilly established a labor union for women. Despite strikes and efforts to organize, though, union members represented less than 10 percent of the non-farm workforce by 1900.

★ TASK

You are a labor organizer in the late 1800s, and you are encouraging your coworkers to go on strike. You are writing a handbill (flyer) to distribute. Write the handbill using historical facts as the basis for your information. The handbill will explain the reason for the strike, the company that is the object of the strike, what the strike hopes to gain for the workers, and when the strike is to take place. In your handbill, try to discourage strikebreakers from taking the place of striking workers, and educate the workers about their rights.

★ AUDIENCE

Workers who receive your handbill are your intended audience.

★ PURPOSE

The purpose of this activity is to organize a strike against a company and to persuade workers to join that strike. Writing the handbill will also give you a greater understanding of why workers rally to support a cause.

★ Performance Assessment Activity 14 (continued)

✪ PROCEDURES

1. Review the background information about unions, the labor movement, and strikes in the late 1800s.

2. Select a strike that you would have supported. Gather as much information about that strike as you can. This information should include the labor organization involved, the decision to strike, working conditions, whether arbitration was used, and whether management issued a blacklist. Use the following lines for your notes.

_____

_____

_____

_____

_____

3. Find examples of handbills, flyers, or posters that have been used to encourage workers to join a union or to strike. Notice how these materials try to motivate people to action.

4. Create a headline for your handbill that will capture the attention of your audience, and write it on the line below.

_____

5. Write an outline of your handbill on the following lines.

_____

_____

_____

_____

6. Write a rough draft of your handbill. Use language that will encourage workers to act, and include facts that will support your strike.

7. Exchange drafts with a classmate for a peer review.

8. Make any necessary revisions, and write your final handbill.

9. Post your handbill on a classroom bulletin board.

✪ ASSESSMENT

1. Use the Assessment Lists suggested to evaluate your handbill.

2. Check to see that you have included all elements; improve as needed.

3. Complete a final self-assessment of your work before you share it.

★ Performance Assessment Activity 15

Use with Chapter 15

Newcomers to American Shores

★ BACKGROUND

In the late 1800s, many immigrants came to the United States from eastern and southern Europe. Some of these immigrants were fleeing wars and political unrest in their native countries. Others wanted religious freedom. Most, though, came to the United States to seek work. After a dangerous Atlantic crossing, most of these immigrants passed through Ellis Island and settled in ethnic neighborhoods in various cities. Other immigrants to the United States, those arriving from China or Japan, crossed the Pacific and were held in barracks on Angel Island. They sometimes spent months in those barracks, waiting for the results of their immigration hearings.

How well immigrants adjusted depended partly on how quickly they could learn English and become Americanized. Some Americans welcomed immigrants. Others, however, disliked this wave of foreigners and wanted to limit immigration. These people, called nativists, were afraid that some of the new arrivals would be political radicals. Others were afraid that immigrants would work for low wages and take jobs away from Americans or that immigrants would become strikebreakers during labor disputes. Because many of the immigrants were Catholic, some feared that the Catholic Church might gain too much power. Prejudice against the immigrants led to the founding of anti-immigrant organizations and stimulated the passage of a federal law designed to ban some immigrants. This law banned convicts, paupers, and the mentally incompetent from immigrating. In 1882 Congress passed the Chinese Exclusion Act, which barred Chinese immigration for 10 years and prevented those Chinese people already in the United States from becoming citizens.

★ TASK

You are a native-born American citizen. You are going to write a letter to the editor of a New York or San Francisco newspaper. In your letter, you will detail either your support for or your dislike of the immigrants you see coming to your city. If you support continued immigration, you will include as many benefits of immigration—both to the new arrivals and to the United States—as you can. If you do not favor immigration, you will give your reasons and support them. Include both facts and personal opinion in your letter to the editor.

★ AUDIENCE

The readers of the newspaper are your intended audience.

★ PURPOSE

The purpose of this activity is to give you experience in writing a letter to the editor. By stating your position and backing that position with facts and personal opinion, you will illustrate your knowledge of immigration during the late 1800s.

★ Performance Assessment Activity 15 (continued)

★ PROCEDURES

1. Review the background information concerning immigration in the late 1800s.

2. Decide whether you support or are opposed to immigration. Write your position on the line below.

   _____

3. Gather as many facts as you can to back your position on immigration. Include facts concerning why immigrants are coming to the United States, where these immigrants are living, and what jobs these immigrants have. Make notes on the following lines.

   _____

   _____

   _____

   _____

4. List your personal opinions concerning immigration and its effect on the United States. Back your opinions with facts if you can. Make notes on the following lines.

   _____

   _____

   _____

   _____

5. List arguments that someone might make against your position. On the following lines, make notes as to how you can rebut these arguments in your letter.

   _____

   _____

   _____

   _____

6. Recall that the format for writing a letter to the editor includes a date, greeting, body, and closing.

7. Write a draft of your letter. Remember to support your position as fully as possible.

8. Give your letter to one of your classmates for peer review.

9. Revise your letter as needed.

★ ASSESSMENT

1. Use the Assessment Lists suggested to evaluate your letter to the editor.

2. Check to see that you have included all elements; improve as needed.

3. Complete a final self-assessment of your work before you share it.

The American Vision

★ Performance Assessment Activity 16

Use with Chapter 16

Join the NAACP

✴ BACKGROUND

In the late 1800s, many African Americans—particularly those in the South—lived in conditions that were little better than slavery. Most were sharecroppers who had to give part of their crops to their landlords for rent, seed, tools, and other supplies. Many African Americans chose to leave the South and moved to Kansas, Oklahoma, and Texas. In 1886 African American activists formed the Colored Farmers' National Alliance. This organization tried to help its members by setting up farming cooperatives and by trying to unite poor white and black farmers to challenge the political leaders in the South.

Southern leaders were trying to separate the races by passing laws that were discriminatory in nature. Rules were passed that barred citizens from voting if they were illiterate or did not own property. Although the rules seemed to apply to people of both races, most whites were given a special break. Grandfather clauses were included in the restrictions. These clauses allowed some people to vote if they met certain existing conditions. One clause, for instance, allowed any man to vote if he had an ancestor on the voting rolls in 1867. Laws were also passed that legalized segregation. After the Civil Rights Act of 1875 was overturned, many private organizations and businesses were free to practice segregation. For the most part, the law upheld the "separate but equal" doctrine. However, public facilities in the South were nearly always separate but unequal. Racial violence against African Americans escalated, and lynchings became common. Some African Americans chose to protest these policies by crusading against the lynchings. Others focused on education, economic goals, and civil rights. In 1909 African Americans such as W.E.B. Du Bois and Ida Wells and several white reformers founded the National Association for the Advancement of Colored People (NAACP). The NAACP attacked racial discrimination and worked to overturn statutes that enforced segregation.

✴ TASK

You are one of the founders of the NAACP. Some of the other members have asked you to write a speech and then use that speech to recruit membership in the NAACP. You will speak to various groups to tell them why the NAACP was formed and what you hope the organization will achieve. Your goal is to convince your audience that joining the NAACP will be to their benefit and the benefit of the country.

✴ AUDIENCE

Poor African Americans and white Americans are your intended audience.

✴ PURPOSE

The purpose of this activity is to give you experience in writing and giving a speech. The purpose of the speech is to increase membership in the NAACP.

★ Performance Assessment Activity 16 (continued)

✪ PROCEDURES

1. Review the background information concerning segregation and discrimination in the United States during the late 1800s.

2. Summarize the events leading up to the formation of the NAACP. Include information concerning the exodus to Kansas, the Colored Farmers' National Alliance, Jim Crow laws, laws that prohibited African Americans from voting, and lynchings. Make notes on the following lines.

_____

_____

_____

_____

_____

_____

_____

_____

3. Mention prominent African American leaders and their responses to racial discrimination and segregation. Make notes on the following lines.

_____

_____

_____

_____

_____

4. Discuss the formation of the NAACP, its members, and its goals. Give reasons why poor whites and African Americans should join the organization. Use the following lines for your notes.

_____

_____

_____

_____

5. Make an outline of your speech, including an introduction and concluding remarks.

6. Write a draft of your speech and give it to a classmate for peer review.

7. Make any necessary revisions and write your speech.

✪ ASSESSMENT

1. Use the Assessment Lists suggested to evaluate your speech.

2. Check to see that you have included all elements; improve as needed.

3. Complete a final self-assessment of your work before you share it.

★ Performance Assessment Activity 17

Use with Chapter 17

The Panama Canal

★ BACKGROUND

Theodore Roosevelt's exploits during the Spanish-American War made him a national hero. In the election of 1900, President McKinley—who was running against William Jennings Bryan—asked Roosevelt to run with him. McKinley won the election, and Roosevelt became vice president. When President McKinley was assassinated, Theodore Roosevelt, at the age of 42, became the youngest person ever to become president. Like McKinley, Roosevelt believed that America should become a world power and influence events in other countries. He believed that all countries should be allowed to trade with China. Roosevelt also helped to negotiate an agreement between Russia and Japan after war broke out between them in 1904.

Roosevelt viewed the construction of a canal through Central America as being vital to American interests. A canal in that region would not only save time and money when shipping goods, but it could also be useful for wartime shipping. A French company had begun digging a canal through Panama in 1881, but it had been forced to stop because of bankruptcy and terrible losses from disease among workers. In 1903 Panama was still part of Colombia. Secretary of State John Hay offered $10 million and a yearly rent of $250,000 for the right to build a canal, but the Colombian government refused. The Panamanians revolted. After the revolt, the United States recognized Panama as an independent country, and they signed a treaty that allowed the canal to be built. The construction began in 1904 and lasted 10 years. More than 40,000 workers built the canal at a cost of nearly $390 million. Accidents and disease caused the deaths of 5,609 workers. When it was finished, the Panama Canal shortened the distance from the Atlantic to the Pacific by about 8,000 nautical miles.

★ TASK

You are going to create a display on the construction of the Panama Canal. Your display should include a time line of events leading up to the involvement of the United States in building the canal, a map showing the advantages of having a canal in Central America, and a diagram or model of how the canal was built. Your display will be exhibited as part of your public library's tribute to the presidency of Theodore Roosevelt.

★ AUDIENCE

The patrons of the public library are your intended audience.

★ PURPOSE

The purpose of this activity is to give you experience in creating a display and to inform people about the Panama Canal.

★ Performance Assessment Activity 17 (continued)

✪ PROCEDURES

1. Review information on the events leading up to the building of the canal. Your information will include background on the attempts of France to build a canal, the revolt in Panama, and the beginnings of American involvement in the construction of the canal. Make notes on the following lines.

_____

_____

_____

_____

2. Consult as many sources as you can to find specific information on the construction of the Panama Canal, including hardships faced by the workers and statistics concerning the canal. Make notes on the following lines.

_____

_____

_____

_____

_____

_____

_____

_____

_____

_____

_____

3. Write a title for your display on the following line.

_____

4. Find the resources needed to create the map showing how the canal would be useful to the United States.

5. Find the resources needed to draw the diagram or build the model of the canal.

6. Put all the elements of your display together to make an attractive and useful presentation.

7. Present your display to your class for evaluation.

✪ ASSESSMENT

1. Use the Assessment Lists suggested to evaluate your display.

2. Check to see that you have included all elements; improve as needed.

3. Complete a final self-assessment of your work before you share it.

★ Performance Assessment Activity 18

Use with Chapter 18

Progressive Campaigns

★ BACKGROUND

Toward the end of the 1800s, the United States faced many problems that had been caused by rapid industrialization and urban growth. A diverse group of reformers known as progressives led one of the most important reform movements in American history. Some progressives feared that too much power in the hands of too few businesspeople would be detrimental to American citizens. Therefore, they argued that no large company should dominate any industry. Progressives advocated peaceful change. Some were writers who used their talents to comment on America's problems, hoping that others would respond to these conditions and bring about change. Some progressives worked to reform city government and politics. Others were concerned about social welfare. Progressives worked to bring about changes in health and safety codes. In the early 1900s, progressives established a National Child Labor Committee to campaign for the abolition of child labor. To protect other workers, progressives joined with labor union leaders to pressure state legislatures for workers' compensation laws. In order to lessen the problems caused by alcohol abuse, some progressives worked to reduce—and later ban—the use of alcohol.

Members of the National American Woman Suffrage Association (NAWSA) worked to give women the right to vote. Members lobbied lawmakers, organized marches, and delivered speeches on street corners. Some members, led by a Quaker social worker named Alice Paul, even chained themselves to lampposts and went on hunger strikes, although not all members of the NAWSA agreed with her tactics. Finally, on August 26, 1920, the Nineteenth Amendment—which guaranteed women the right to vote—went into effect.

★ TASK

You are going to create an original political cartoon to be published in a newspaper. Your cartoon will comment on the Progressive movement and its goals. You will focus on one aspect of the Progressive movement and illustrate that aspect in your cartoon. Your cartoon will include an original drawing and a caption. You may include dialogue with your cartoon if you wish to do so. Plan to create a title for your cartoon.

★ AUDIENCE

The readers of the newspaper are your intended audience.

★ PURPOSE

The purpose of this activity is to give you experience in creating a political cartoon. It will also highlight one of the objectives of the Progressive movement.

★ **Performance Assessment Activity 18** (continued)

◪ PROCEDURES

1. Review the background information concerning the Progressive movement at the end of the 1800s and the beginning of the 1900s. Focus your attention on political and social reforms championed by the progressives.

2. Choose an event or topic related to the Progressive movement that interests you and that you will use as the basis of your cartoon. Write your topic on the following line.

_____

3. Conduct further research to learn more about your topic.

4. Find examples of political cartoons and review the techniques used in political cartooning. Remember that caricatures and symbols are often used in political cartoons to communicate the message. Make notes on your ideas for your political cartoon on the lines below.

_____

_____

_____

_____

_____

_____

5. Sketch your cartoon.

6. On the following lines, write the dialogue you will use in your cartoon. Also write the caption that will accompany your cartoon.

_____

_____

_____

_____

7. Create a title for your cartoon and write it on the lines below.

_____

_____

_____

8. Share your work with a partner for comments and suggestions.

9. Make the final copy of your cartoon.

◪ ASSESSMENT

1. Use the Assessment Lists suggested to evaluate your political cartoon.

2. Check to see that you have included all elements; improve as needed.

3. Complete a final self-assessment of your work before you share it.

The American Vision

★ Performance Assessment Activity 19

Use with Chapter 19

Post-World War I Chart

⊠ BACKGROUND

At the end of World War I, the American people experienced a series of domestic problems. One of these problems was an economic recession. During the war, federal agencies had directed the war effort and had employed thousands of workers. When the war ended, these agencies closed suddenly, and many people lost their jobs. Strikes broke out across the country as labor unions, which had increased their membership during the war, tried to hold onto the gains they had made for their members. Police officers, coal miners, and steelworkers unions went on strike. As American soldiers returned home from Europe, they discovered that they now had to compete with African Americans for jobs and housing. Increased tensions sometimes led to racial violence. In addition, a panic known as the Red Scare swept through America. Many Americans believed that Communists were going to take over the country. This led to the persecution of many of the nation's workers and immigrants. In the spring of 1919, the postal service discovered that dozens of packages addressed to leading businesspeople had been rigged to explode. One of these packages had been addressed to Attorney General A. Mitchell Palmer. Palmer established a special division within the Justice Department to seek out political and labor agitators all over the country. These raids were carried out with no regard for the civil liberties of the suspects. Nearly 600 people were deported, some without the benefit of trials. Although not everyone agreed with Palmer's tactics, for awhile he was seen as a national hero. By 1920 economic problems, labor unrest, racial tensions, and the Red Scare combined to create a sense of disillusionment. Many Americans hoped for a calmer future and were eager for a sense of stability to return. They were tired of crusades to reform society and the world.

⊠ TASK

You are going to create a chart that illustrates the state of Americans and the American economy after World War I. Your chart will include strong graphic elements to provide clarity and get people's attention. The chart will include information on postwar labor unrest, racial unrest, the Red Scare, and the Palmer raids.

⊠ AUDIENCE

The members of your class are your intended audience.

⊠ PURPOSE

The purpose of this activity is to highlight and summarize factors that were critical to Americans in the aftermath of World War I. You will also gain experience in organizing information in a chart form.

★ Performance Assessment Activity 19 (continued)

✪ PROCEDURES

1. Review the background information concerning factors in American life in the aftermath of World War I.

2. Make an outline for your chart on the following lines. Include the heads and any subheads that you will use. Clarifying subheads will allow you to do further research.

_____

_____

_____

_____

_____

_____

_____

3. Organize your information under four headings—Labor Unrest, Racial Unrest, Red Scare, and Palmer Raids. Write a rough draft of the information that will appear on your chart.

4. Create a title for your chart and record it on the following lines.

_____

_____

5. Make notes on ideas that can add interest to your chart, such as using drawings, color, or graphic elements. Make notes on the lines below.

_____

_____

_____

_____

_____

6. Make a rough sketch of the chart, and indicate the visual elements you will include. You may use photocopies of illustrations you find in other sources, or you may create illustrations of your own.

7. Exchange your draft with a partner for comments and suggestions.

8. Make any changes you think are necessary, and then make your final chart.

✪ ASSESSMENT

1. Use the Assessment Lists suggested to evaluate your chart.

2. Check to see that you have included all elements; improve as needed.

3. Complete a final self-assessment of your work before you share it.

★ Performance Assessment Activity 20

Use with Chapter 20

The Harlem Renaissance

✚ BACKGROUND

The 1920s witnessed vibrant changes in art and literature. During World War I, many African Americans moved North to escape segregation and to search for better employment opportunities. This movement was called the Great Migration. In the neighborhood of Harlem in New York City, African Americans from the South gathered together to share their experiences. In doing so, they created an environment that was favorable to artistic development, racial pride, a sense of community, and political organization. This became known as the Harlem Renaissance. Harlem became a beacon for African American writers, musicians, and entertainers. Poets such as Langston Hughes and Claude McKay wrote about the African American experience in America. Countee Cullen, Alain Locke, and Zora Neale Hurston influenced later generations of African American writers like Toni Morrison and Ralph Ellison. Louis Armstrong introduced an improvisational, early form of jazz and later became jazz music's first great cornet and trumpet soloist. People danced to the music of bandleader Duke Ellington. Bessie Smith became known as the "Empress of the Blues" for her emotional and dramatic style of singing. Paul Robeson, a celebrated singer and actor, often appeared at the Apollo Theater in Harlem. Robeson became famous for his work in the musical *Show Boat*. His fame eventually spread to Europe, where he starred in the London production of Shakespeare's *Othello*. Josephine Baker, a singer and dancer whose style was very flamboyant for the time, performed on Broadway and in the floor show at Harlem's Plantation Club. She later went to Paris, where she danced in *La Revue Negre*, a musical review featuring black performers.

✚ TASK

You are going to write a biographical sketch of one of the leaders of the Harlem Renaissance. Your article, which will be a minimum of three pages long, will appear in a literary magazine. In your article, you will include background information on the Great Migration and the Harlem Renaissance. You will choose a writer, a musician, or an actor and explore that person's contribution to the Harlem Renaissance in depth.

✚ AUDIENCE

The readers of the literary magazine are your intended audience.

✚ PURPOSE

The purpose of this activity is to give you experience in writing a biographical sketch. Your goal is to give your readers a greater understanding of the life of your chosen artist and his or her contributions to the Harlem Renaissance.

★ **Performance Assessment Activity 20** (continued)

✪ PROCEDURES

1. Review information concerning the Great Migration and the Harlem Renaissance. Consult as many original sources as possible.

2. Decide who will be the topic of your biographical sketch. Write the name of that person on the following line.

   _____

3. Discover as much information on your choice as possible. Include place and date of birth, childhood circumstances, and migration to the North, if appropriate. Make notes on the following lines.

   _____

   _____

   _____

   _____

4. List the contributions your person made to the Harlem Renaissance. Be as specific with your information as possible. Remember to include citations in your biographical sketch if you use work from other sources. If possible, find a photo to include with your article. Make notes on the following lines.

   _____

   _____

   _____

   _____

5. Include information concerning the later life and death of the person you chose. If you can, list the names of current writers, artists, or musicians who name the person as his or her influence. Make notes on the following lines.

   _____

   _____

   _____

   _____

6. Write a rough draft of your biographical sketch. Trade articles with a classmate for a peer review.

7. Make any necessary revisions, and complete your biographical sketch.

✪ ASSESSMENT

1. Use the Assessment Lists suggested to evaluate your biographical sketch.

2. Check to see that you have included all elements; improve as needed.

3. Complete a final self-assessment of your work before you share it.

★ Performance Assessment Activity 21

Use with Chapter 21

Help Wanted

★ BACKGROUND

In the 1920s, the United States experienced rapid economic growth. Wages increased, and work hours decreased. With more money to spend and more leisure time, Americans looked for ways to improve their lifestyles. For the first time, automobiles became available to the majority of American consumers. Henry Ford, a Michigan carmaker, used the assembly line method of auto production to make the industry more efficient. Car-making was divided into simple tasks that unskilled workers could perform. Ford's car—the Model T—sold for $850 in 1908. By 1924 production of the Model T had become so efficient that the cars sold for $295. Thousands of cars were sold. With increasing sales, Ford implemented a bonus system for his workers so that they could earn extra money. He also reduced the workday to 8-hour shifts. This created a very loyal workforce. However, Ford expected workers to lead model lives, and he set up a Sociological Department to make sure that they did. Investigators were sent to the homes of employees to make sure that they were spending money wisely and in Ford-approved ways. If they were not, employees might be disqualified for bonuses, suspended, or even fired.

Cars completely changed the American way of life. They eased the isolation felt by people who lived in rural areas. Small businesses such as garages and gas stations were started to support the automotive industry. Because people were now able to live farther away from work than they had in the past, a new kind of worker—the auto commuter—appeared. Commuters often lived in suburban communities and drove to work in the city. A rise in suburban living followed shortly.

★ TASK

You work in the personnel department of the Highland Park, Michigan, Ford company. You need to write a help-wanted ad that will appear in the local newspaper. The company needs to hire several unskilled workers to perform tasks on the Ford assembly line. In your ad, you will include information concerning work hours, wages, working conditions, the product (the Model T, or "Tin Lizzie"), and benefits such as bonuses and job satisfaction. Because your ad has no size limit, you may also include a drawing of a Model T.

★ AUDIENCE

The readers of the newspaper are your intended audience.

★ PURPOSE

The purpose of this activity is to give you experience in writing a help-wanted ad and to learn more about the automobile industry in the early 1900s.

★ Performance Assessment Activity 21 (continued)

✪ PROCEDURES

1. Review information concerning the automobile industry in the early 1900s. Focus specifically on the Ford company and the techniques used on Ford's assembly line.

2. List the tasks performed on Ford's assembly line. Make notes on the following lines.

_____

_____

_____

_____

3. In your ad, include information concerning working conditions, wages, and work hours for assembly-line workers. Make notes on the following lines.

_____

_____

_____

_____

4. List the benefits available to assembly-line workers. Present these benefits in the most positive light possible. Make notes on the following lines.

_____

_____

_____

_____

5. Look at current help-wanted ads for the automotive industry. If possible, find an original Ford ad and an illustration of a Model T. You may use these ideas or illustrations in your ad.

6. Write a rough draft of your help-wanted ad. Trade ads with a classmate for a peer review.

7. After making any necessary revisions, write your help-wanted ad.

✪ ASSESSMENT

1. Use the Assessment Lists suggested to evaluate your help-wanted ad.

2. Check to see that you have included all elements; improve as needed.

3. Complete a final self-assessment of your work before you share it.

★ **Performance Assessment Activity 22**

Use with Chapter 22

Pictures of the Great Depression

✪ BACKGROUND

During the Great Depression, life was difficult for many people. As the Depression worsened, banks across the nation went out of business. By 1933 more than 9,000 banks had failed and billions of dollars in people's savings were lost. Farm income dropped, and many companies went out of business. Workers lost their jobs, and those who were still employed often had only part-time work. People without jobs often went hungry. Whenever possible, they lined up outside soup kitchens or joined bread lines in order to get enough to eat. Many people were ashamed that they had been reduced to such circumstances. Some who could no longer pay rent or pay the mortgage lost their homes and were forced to live in communities called shanty-towns, or Hoovervilles. Others became hobos and roamed the country.

Beginning in 1932, a terrible drought came to the Great Plains. The drought caused crops to fail. Soon the soil turned to dust, and the land from the Dakotas to Texas turned into a vast Dust Bowl. Many farmers packed their belongings into old cars or trucks and headed west. Because many of these farmers were from Oklahoma, they became known as "Okies." Soon the homeless and the jobless became the subject of photos and stories as artists and writers tried to capture the life they were seeing around them. Writers like John Steinbeck and Thomas Wolfe wrote about the hardships people faced. Artists like Edward Hopper and Grant Wood tried to capture the isolation and loneliness of Depression life. Magazine photographers roamed the nation taking photos that showed the ravages of the drought and its effect on people. Photographers such as Margaret Bourke-White and Walker Evans were among those whose photos created a record of life during the Great Depression.

✪ TASK

You are going to create a photo essay to present to your classmates. Your subject is life during the Great Depression. You will use books, magazines, newspapers, or Internet sites as the primary sources for your photos. You will locate photos of people and places taken during the Great Depression, create a title for each photo, and write a brief description of the photo in a summary paragraph. The title and summary paragraphs will be written on index cards. Information specific to each photo should be included on the summary cards, as well as any information that you can find about each photographer. The photos and your summary paragraphs will be part of a classroom display on the Great Depression.

✪ AUDIENCE

Your classmates are your intended audience.

★ Performance Assessment Activity 22 (continued)

✪ PURPOSE

The purpose of this activity is to create a visual presentation of life during the Great Depression.

✪ PROCEDURES

1. Review information concerning daily life during the Great Depression.

2. Using the library or the Internet to seek out books, magazines, newspaper articles, and photos about the Great Depression. From these sources, choose a minimum of six photos. On the following lines, list the six photos you have chosen.

_____

_____

_____

_____

_____

_____

3. Gather as much information as you can about each photo. List the photographer if that information is available, the subject matter of the photo, and any pertinent information you can find about events leading up to when the photo was taken. Make notes on the following lines.

_____

_____

_____

_____

_____

_____

4. Summarize your notes on index cards. Make sure that your comments are descriptive and easy to read. Write a title for each photo at the top of each index card.

5. Trade index cards and photos with a classmate. Ask your classmate for any comments or suggestions as to how to make your summaries more clear.

6. Write your final summaries.

7. Your summaries will be placed below the photos on a display table in your classroom.

✪ ASSESSMENT

1. Use the Assessment Lists suggested to evaluate your photo essay.

2. Check to see that you have included all elements; improve as needed.

3. Complete a final self-assessment of your work before you share it.

★ Performance Assessment Activity 23

Use with Chapter 23

The First 100 Days

★ BACKGROUND

During the first 100 days of Franklin D. Roosevelt's presidency, he and his team initiated a series of laws that led to the establishment of a wide variety of federal agencies. The new president sent bill after bill to Congress, and Congress acted quickly. Roosevelt hoped to establish these agencies to help Americans recover from the Great Depression and to regain their faith in government. The day after he took office, Roosevelt declared a bank holiday. He temporarily closed all the banks and then passed the Emergency Banking Relief Act. This act allowed banks to reopen under the eye of federal examiners. Roosevelt talked with the American people through a series of "fireside chats," where he told people in simple language that their money would be okay if they put it back into the banks. Roosevelt's programs helped farmers with their debt problems and assisted homeowners so that more could afford houses. The Glass-Steagall Act prohibited commercial banks from risking their depositor's money, and the Federal Deposit Insurance Corporation (FDIC) was formed to provide government insurance for savings accounts. Roosevelt moved to protect investors from fraud. He also initiated many spending and relief programs, including the Civilian Conservation Corps (CCC), the Federal Emergency Relief Administration (FEMA), the Civil Works Administration (CWA) and the Public Works Administration (PWA). These programs created thousands of jobs for the unemployed. Roosevelt was also interested in long-term economic and social planning. The Agricultural Adjustment Act and the National Industrial Recovery Act were both aimed for long-term results. Roosevelt also created the Tennessee Valley Authority (TVA) to build dams, reforest land, build power plants and factories, and start new towns.

★ TASK

You are an editor for a newspaper in 1933, at the end of Roosevelt's first 100 days. You are going to publish a tribute to Franklin D. Roosevelt. Your tribute will include Roosevelt's challenges and accomplishments.

★ AUDIENCE

The readers of the newspaper are the intended audience.

★ PURPOSE

The purpose of this activity is to give you experience in writing a tribute and to learn more about the sweeping changes introduced by Franklin D. Roosevelt.

★ Performance Assessment Activity 23 (continued)

★ PROCEDURES

1. Review the background information concerning President Franklin D. Roosevelt and his first 100 days in office.

2. Use as many sources as possible to research additional information. Include details about the problems Roosevelt faced when he took office, the bills that he and his team sent to Congress, and the laws that have been enacted as a result of those bills. Beside each law, indicate what agency was established because of that law and what that agency is intended to accomplish. Make notes on the following lines.

_____

_____

_____

_____

_____

_____

_____

_____

_____

3. Find at least one quotation from Franklin D. Roosevelt to include in your tribute, and write it on the lines below.

_____

_____

4. Write an outline of your tribute on the lines below. Create a headline that will get the attention of your readers, and include that headline on the following lines.

_____

_____

_____

_____

5. Write a rough draft of your tribute.

6. Exchange your rough draft with a classmate for peer review.

7. Write your final newspaper tribute after making any necessary revisions.

★ ASSESSMENT

1. Use the Assessment Lists suggested to evaluate your newspaper tribute.

2. Check to see that you have included all elements; improve as needed.

3. Complete a final self-assessment of your work before you share it.

★ Performance Assessment Activity 24

Use with Chapter 24

Attack!

★ BACKGROUND

Between 1939 and December 1941, President Roosevelt had tried to help Great Britain and its allies defeat Germany. Britain needed to keep much of its navy in Southeast Asia to protect British interests there from attack by Japan. When German submarines began sinking British ships, the British began moving their ships to the Atlantic, which left their empire open to attack. Roosevelt tried to help Britain by putting economic pressures on Japan. He blocked the sale of airplane fuel, scrap iron, and other materials to Japan, and he began to aid China. He also sent General Douglas MacArthur to the Philippines to build up American defenses there. In 1941 Roosevelt reduced all oil shipments to Japan. Roosevelt planned to lift the oil embargo only if Japan withdrew troops from Southeast Asia and made peace with China. The Japanese military began to make plans to attack the British and Dutch colonies in Southeast Asia, seize the Philippines, and attack the American fleet at Pearl Harbor. If the American fleet could be destroyed, then Japan would not have to worry about American interference in its plans in Southeast Asia. On November 26, 1941, six Japanese aircraft carriers, two battleships, and several other warships set sail for Hawaii. The Americans had intercepted and decoded some Japanese communications, and these decoded messages made it quite clear that Japan was preparing to go to war against the United States. However, Hawaii was not mentioned as a specific target. On December 7, 1941, Japan launched a surprise attack against American forces in Pearl Harbor. The attack destroyed 21 ships of the U.S. Pacific Fleet and 188 airplanes. Nearly 2,500 Americans were killed, and another 1,178 Americans were injured. The following day, President Roosevelt asked Congress to declare war on Japan.

★ TASK

You are the disc jockey in Pearl Harbor's only radio station on the morning of December 7, 1941. As the morning progresses, people begin to call the station with news of a Japanese aerial attack. You also begin to receive news by teletype (a machine similar to a typewriter that can receive printed messages from news sources outside Hawaii). You decide to provide coverage of the attack for your listeners—as long as you can stay on the air. You will write a script for a radio announcement about the attack. You will give periodic updates throughout the morning concerning events that are occurring in Pearl Harbor. You will also give out information concerning emergency procedures for the civilian population of Pearl Harbor.

★ AUDIENCE

Listeners of your radio station are your intended audience.

★ Performance Assessment Activity 24 (continued)

★ PURPOSE

The purpose of this activity is to recreate a 1941 radio broadcast about the Japanese attack on Pearl Harbor. Your goal is to make your broadcast as accurate and true to life as possible.

★ PROCEDURES

1. Review information about Pearl Harbor on December 7, 1941. Research information on the layout of Pearl Harbor, the names of the ships in the harbor, the number of airplanes, the number of military personnel, and any other information you can find concerning that morning.

2. Search out tapes or transcripts of radio announcements from a museum of television and radio, if possible, or find descriptions of radio shows to learn about the broadcast style that was used in 1941. Listen to contemporary radio shows to get other ideas.

3. Decide on the information that you will broadcast. Make notes on the lines below.

_____

_____

_____

_____

_____

_____

_____

_____

_____

_____

4. Write a rough draft of the script of your broadcast. Give the rough draft to a classmate for a peer review.

5. Make any necessary changes to the script of your broadcast.

6. Practice reading the script aloud. Make your voice convey the emotion that you are feeling.

7. Perform your broadcast for a classmate. Ask him or her to give you feedback about your voice, the speed at which you are reading your broadcast, and any other suggestions your classmate might have.

8. Perform your broadcast in front of the class.

★ ASSESSMENT

1. Use the Assessment Lists suggested to evaluate your radio broadcast.

2. Check to see that you have included all elements; improve as needed.

3. Complete a final self-assessment of your work before you share it.

The American Vision

★ Performance Assessment Activity 25

Use with Chapter 25

Here at Home

★ BACKGROUND

World War II had a positive effect on the American economy and finally put an end to the Great Depression. Millions of new jobs were created to support the war effort, and the average family's income nearly doubled. The war did, however, lead to hardships at home. Although new jobs were created, many Americans did not live close to these locations. Many people had to move, and this caused a housing crisis. Racial tensions increased. African Americans were often looked upon with suspicion and mistrust when they moved North to take new jobs. Japanese Americans were forced into internment camps, where they lived until early 1945. Because of the high demand for workers and raw materials, prices of goods at home continued to rise. Roosevelt urged wage and price controls to combat inflation. Shortages of raw materials and supplies led to rationing, or limiting the amount of a good that was available to consumers. Ration coupons were used in every household to purchase such items as meats, sugar, and coffee. Driving was restricted to save gasoline and rubber. Americans planted victory gardens to produce more food for the war effort. Backyards, schoolyards, parks, and empty lots were planted with fruits and vegetables. Certain materials were so vital to the war effort that the government organized scrap drives. Americans donated such things as pots and pans, rusty bicycles, and tin cans to the war effort. Oils and fats, which were needed to create explosives, were collected also. Bacon grease and meat drippings could be exchanged for extra ration coupons. Despite all these hardships, nearly all Americans believed that the war should be fought, and they wholly supported the war effort. Patriotism ran high, and Americans were eager to do their part.

★ TASK

As a student attending school in 1942, you have been asked to contribute your songwriting talents in support of the war. Your job is to write the lyrics for a patriotic song that will inspire civilians to support the war effort at home. Your song will include at least four verses and a refrain. If you like, you can set your lyrics to music. You will present your lyrics to the members of the student body at a meeting called to discuss the war effort.

★ AUDIENCE

Your audience is the student body of your school.

★ PURPOSE

The purpose of this activity is to write a patriotic song that will encourage people to work for the war effort on the home front.

★ Performance Assessment Activity 25 (continued)

✪ PROCEDURES

1. Review the background information concerning the war effort on the home front during World War II.

2. Conduct further research to find examples of patriotic songs from World War II. Note different slogans that were popular and how these slogans were used to sway public opinion.

3. On the lines below, list the topic of your song and the actions you are encouraging people to take.

_____

_____

_____

_____

_____

_____

_____

_____

4. On the following lines, list some key words or phrases that you want to include in your song.

_____

_____

_____

_____

_____

_____

5. Write a rough draft of your song. Continue to make revisions until you are satisfied that the song is both inspiring and interesting.

6. Give your draft—or sing your song—to a classmate for comments and suggestions.

7. Make any revisions that you think are appropriate, and make a final copy of your song. If you wish, you can also set it to music and record it.

8. Read the lyrics, sing the song, or play the tape of your song to the student body. Submit a copy of the lyrics to your teacher.

✪ ASSESSMENT

1. Use the Assessment Lists suggested to evaluate your patriotic song.

2. Check to see that you have included all elements; improve as needed.

3. Complete a final self-assessment of your work before you share it.

The American Vision

★ **Performance Assessment Activity 26**

Use with Chapter 26

The Rosenbergs

★ BACKGROUND

Following World War II, the United States enjoyed peace, but fears of communism often overshadowed day-to-day life. Reports that the Soviets had detonated an atomic bomb and that the Soviet Union was carrying on espionage in the United States tapped into people's fears about a Communist takeover. Between 1947 and 1951, the FBI ran checks on 6 million federal employees to determine whether they were loyal to the United States. A person might become suspect for reading certain books, belonging to various organizations or groups, traveling overseas, or even seeing a foreign film. In Hollywood, members of the House Un-American Activities Committee (HUAC) questioned screenwriters, actors, and directors about their loyalty to the country. Hollywood producers drew up a list of people whose loyalty HUAC felt was in question and agreed not to hire those people. Many careers were ruined. Public anxiety about a possible Communist conspiracy to take over the United States kept growing, and increased fears about Communist spying kept the country on edge. One of the most sensational spy cases involved Julius and Ethel Rosenberg, a New York couple who were members of the Communist Party. The Rosenbergs were charged with heading a spy ring that was stealing atomic secrets and passing them to the Communists. The Rosenbergs denied the charges. Some people believed that they were not spies but that they had been caught up in the wave of anticommunist feeling. The Rosenbergs were found guilty. There were public expressions of support and pleas for clemency, but they were sentenced to death. Julius and Ethel Rosenberg were executed in June 1953.

★ TASK

You are going to participate in a mock trial with four other students in your class. Two students will assume the roles of Julius and Ethel Rosenberg, one student will assume the role of the prosecutor, one student will be the defense attorney, and one student will act as the judge. Each student will research information about his or her role and then present that information during the trial. The judge will act as moderator; the jury will be the members of your class.

★ AUDIENCE

The members of your class are your intended audience.

★ PURPOSE

The purpose of this activity is to research the Rosenberg trial and then hold a mock trial to see if your jury returns the same verdict that the actual Rosenberg jury returned.

★ **Performance Assessment Activity 26 (continued)**

✪ PROCEDURES

1. Research information about the events that were occurring in the United States during the late 1940s and early 1950s. Gather background information on the Red Scare and the fears of the American public concerning Communist spies.

2. Decide which member of your group will be the prosecutor, the defense attorney, the judge, and Julius and Ethel Rosenberg. Write the names and roles on the lines below.

_____

_____

_____

3. Each member of the group should research his or her role extensively. Find as many original documents as possible to support each role. Use the following lines to make notes about your role. For example, if you are the prosecutor, list the questions you will ask. If you are one of the Rosenbergs, list how you will respond to anticipated questions. If you are the defense attorney, list points you will try to make to defend your clients. Be as specific as possible.

_____

_____

_____

_____

_____

_____

_____

_____

_____

_____

_____

4. Practice your mock trial in front of a few classmates. Ask for their feedback and suggestions.

5. Write your notes in a format that you can easily understand. You will need to locate facts quickly during the mock trial. Make sure your notes are well organized.

6. Present your mock trial in front of your classmates (your jury).

7. Ask your classmates to vote on the outcome of your mock trial.

8. Turn your notes in to your teacher.

✪ ASSESSMENT

1. Use the Assessment Lists suggested to evaluate your mock trial.

2. Check to see that you have included all elements; improve as needed.

3. Complete a final self-assessment of your work before you share it.

★ **Performance Assessment Activity 27**

Use with Chapter 27

The Wealth of America

★ BACKGROUND

Although most Americans were enjoying great prosperity in the years following World War II, that prosperity did not extend to everyone. Many Americans found themselves living below the poverty line, a figure that reflected the minimum income needed to support a family. As white families moved to the suburbs, inner cities became havens for minorities who were usually poorer and less educated than their white counterparts. Numerous factories and mills relocated, and African Americans and Hispanics struggled to find work and support themselves. Native Americans, who constituted less than one percent of the population by the mid-1900s, were encouraged to assimilate into white society whether they wanted to or not. Native Americans moved off the reservations and into the cities under a plan that became known as the termination policy. The policy proved to be disastrous for many Native Americans.

The economic boom also bypassed Appalachia. People living in Appalachia were often impoverished and suffered from a lack of medical attention. Rates of nutritional deficiency and infant mortality were high. The country also suffered from an increase in juvenile delinquency and other crimes, although Americans could not seem to agree on what caused these problems. Some blamed them on a lack of parental discipline, while others blamed drugs and alcohol. Although most teenagers steered clear of gangs and drugs, the public tended to stereotype young people with long hair and unconventional clothing as delinquents. Many Americans also feared that their children were not learning enough in school. As baby boomers began entering school, shortages of both buildings and teachers occurred. Parents were afraid that their children might fall behind those of the Soviet Union—particularly in the areas of reading, math, and science.

★ TASK

You are an author who plans to write a short story about the Americans who were *not* part of the economic boom that occurred after World War II. Your story will be read by juveniles, or people between the ages of 10 and 15. Your story will be fiction, although it will be based on historic fact. Your characters and plot will reflect the views and actions of a group of people during the postwar years. Your short story will be a minimum of four pages long.

★ AUDIENCE

Your audience is juveniles who will read your published story.

★ PURPOSE

The purpose of this activity is to present a historically correct, fictional account of the life of a person or group during the post-World War II period. The people you choose will not be part of the economic boom. Your story will illustrate the problems faced by these people or groups and lead to a greater understanding of problems faced by some in the mid-1900s.

★ Performance Assessment Activity 27 (continued)

✪ PROCEDURES

1. Review the background information about the people and groups who were *not* part of the post-World War II economic boom. You may find additional sources in your school library.

2. Choose the group that you will use as the subject for your story. For example, you may choose people living in Appalachia, Native Americans living in the inner city, or juvenile delinquents. Your story may include references to more than one issue, but it should center on only one main theme. List the group that you plan to use in your story on the line below.

   _____

3. Research to find more facts about your group. Search out materials that offer first-person accounts, biographies, or autobiographies. Make important notes on the following lines.

   _____

   _____

   _____

   _____

4. Recall that in historical fiction, the author places fictitious characters and events in historically accurate settings.

5. On the lines below, outline your story for the purpose of showing where you will use historical facts.

   _____

   _____

   _____

   _____

   _____

   _____

6. Write a rough draft of your story, using narrative and dialogue. Write a title that gives a clue about the story's subject on the line below.

   _____

7. Exchange drafts with a classmate for a peer review. Make any necessary revisions, and write the final draft of your story.

8. Read your short story to your class.

✪ ASSESSMENT

1. Use the Assessment Lists suggested to evaluate your historical fiction.

2. Check to see that you have included all elements; improve as needed.

3. Complete a final self-assessment of your work before you share it.

The American Vision

★ **Performance Assessment Activity 28**

Use with Chapter 28

One Person, One Vote

✪ BACKGROUND

In the election of 1960, Richard Nixon, the Republican candidate, ran against John Kennedy, a Democrat. Richard Nixon, who was from California, was a Quaker whose family had often faced financial struggles. He was hardworking and serious and had a reputation as being tough on communism. Nixon, who had long been a member of Congress, had served as vice president under Eisenhower and had easily won his party's nomination for president. Kennedy, like Nixon, was a member of Congress. However, he had faced heavy competition in his race for the Democratic nomination. Kennedy was a World War II hero with a charismatic family who captured the imagination of the American people. The 1960 campaign centered on the economy and the Cold War with the Soviet Union. Both candidates promised to boost the economy and both were determined to stop the forces of communism. The two men differed, though, on the best way to stop the Communists. Kennedy talked about a "missile gap" and the problems Americans would face if America found itself on the wrong side of the gap. Nixon thought Kennedy was being too pessimistic. Nixon thought America was on the right track with the current administration. Another area of difference between the two men was religion. Kennedy was Catholic, and the United States had never had a Catholic president. During the 1960 campaign, television was used for the first time as a campaign tool. Both candidates spent much money on television ads, and both television and radio broadcast the Kennedy/Nixon debates. Most agreed that Nixon looked uncomfortable on television. Kennedy, on the other hand, came across as being at ease with the cameras, and he made a positive impact on the American viewers.

✪ TASK

As part of your work with a civic organization, you have been asked to prepare a voter's guide to the 1960 presidential election. The guide will present an independent and impartial view of the two candidates. It will include information on each candidate's experience and his positions on domestic policy and foreign policy. Your guide may also include proposed solutions to problems, or explanations of campaign slogans. The guide will be distributed for free in the weeks prior to the election.

✪ AUDIENCE

Your audience is people of voting age in your community.

✪ PURPOSE

The purpose of the voter's guide is to give the public objective information about a candidate that will help them decide for whom to vote.

★ Performance Assessment Activity 28 (continued)

★ PROCEDURES

1. Review information about the 1960 presidential campaign. Gather as much information as you can about Richard Nixon and John Kennedy.

2. Decide which format would be best for your voter's guide. On the following lines, list the questions about the candidates that will be answered in your guide.

   _____

   _____

   _____

   _____

   _____

3. Conduct research to put together your guide. On the following lines, note quotations from each candidate about policies or important events.

   _____

   _____

   _____

   _____

4. Decide what information will be included in your guide. Make sure that you present an objective picture of each candidate.

5. Choose a photograph of each candidate to go in your voter's guide.

6. Write an outline of your voter's guide on the following lines.

   _____

   _____

   _____

   _____

   _____

   _____

   _____

7. Prepare a draft of your guide. Exchange drafts with a classmate for a peer review. Make any necessary revisions to your guide.

8. Write your final version of the voter's guide.

★ ASSESSMENT

1. Use the Assessment Lists suggested to evaluate your voter's guide.

2. Check to see that you have included all elements; improve as needed.

3. Complete a final self-assessment of your work before you share it.

The American Vision

★ Performance Assessment Activity 29

Use with Chapter 29

Sitting In for Freedom

★ BACKGROUND

Although the members of the Congress of Racial Equality (CORE) had used non-violent sit-ins as a form of protest as early as 1942, it was not until 1960 that sit-ins became widely used as a means to fight for equality for African Americans. Beginning with a sit-in at a whites-only lunch counter in a Woolworth's store, the movement spread quickly across the country. The sit-in movement had an energizing effect for many African Americans who had become discouraged by the slow pace of desegregation. At first the leaders of the NAACP and the Southern Christian Leadership Conference (SCLC) were nervous about the sit-in movement, because they were afraid that the participants might lack the self-control to remain nonviolent when provoked by bystanders and police. The sit-ins remained peaceful, however. As the sit-in movement spread to different states, student leaders decided that someone needed to coordinate their efforts. They chose Ella Baker, who was a member of the SCLC. She urged students to create their own organization, which they did. The new student organization was the Student Nonviolent Coordinating Committee (SNCC). The first leader of SNCC was Marion Barry, who later became mayor of Washington, D.C. Most of the members of SNCC were African American college students, but whites were accepted and encouraged to participate. Between 1960 and 1965, SNCC played a key role in forcing dozens of Southern communities to desegregate public facilities. SNCC also spearheaded an effort to register African Americans to vote. Many SNCC volunteers had their lives threatened for their work in the South. In 1964 three SNCC volunteers were brutally murdered by local officials in Mississippi. The civil rights movement later included black nationalists and the black power movement, organizations that moved away from nonviolence.

★ TASK

As a member of the Student Nonviolent Coordinating Committee (SNCC), you will plan and participate in a nonviolent sit-in to demand civil rights for African Americans. You will choose the issue of your protest, make posters, give speeches, and distribute an information flyer. Your sit-in will be based on a historical event in the civil rights movement.

★ AUDIENCE

Your intended audience is lawmakers, politicians, the media, and ordinary citizens.

★ PURPOSE

The purpose of the sit-in is to demand civil rights and to influence public opinion. Planning the sit-in will give you experience in participating in a movement for social change.

★ Performance Assessment Activity 29 (continued)

★ PROCEDURES

1. Review the background information about the civil rights movement.

2. Conduct research about sit-ins in the 1950s and 1960s. Find out where and why they took place, who organized them, who participated, and how long they lasted.

3. Choose the date and location of your sit-in and identify the protest issue. Write this information on the following lines.

_____

_____

_____

_____

_____

4. Decide how you will contribute to the sit-in. You may create a poster, create a placard, write a speech, or write a flyer that will be distributed during the protest. Look at magazines and newspapers for examples of the kinds of posters and signs that were used in the civil rights movement. Create slogans or phrases that focus on your issue. Write your ideas on the lines below.

_____

_____

_____

_____

_____

_____

_____

_____

_____

5. Write a draft of your contribution (poster, placard, speech, flyer). Exchange drafts within your group, and make any necessary revisions.

6. Arrange a date with your teacher to hold your sit-in. Exhibit your posters and placards, pass out your flyers, and give your speeches. Be prepared to answer questions from "passersby," who may be other students in your school.

★ ASSESSMENT

1. Use the Assessment Lists suggested to evaluate your sit-in.

2. Check to see that you have included all elements; improve as needed.

3. Complete a final self-assessment of your work before you share it.

The American Vision

★ Performance Assessment Activity 30

Use with Chapter 30

Vietnam

★ BACKGROUND

When American troops first went to Vietnam in the spring of 1965, most Americans supported the war effort. As the war continued, though, people became suspicious of the government's reporting of events. Footage of combat appeared nightly on the television news. Images of so many dead and wounded soldiers seemed to contradict the government's assertions that America was winning the war. The war also began to hurt the nation's economy. Taxes were increased to help fund the war and to slow the rate of inflation. Many Americans began to question America's role in the war. Soon, an antiwar movement emerged. Many people in the antiwar movement were college students who were not eligible for the draft because of their student status. Although there were some students who supported the war effort, the antiwar faction—which was more vocal—got most of the attention. Student groups such as the Students for a Democratic Society (SDS) organized protests and marches to rally antiwar support. Many pointed to the high number of African Americans and poor Americans who were dying in Vietnam, while people who could afford college did not have to go. Protests against the war were not confined to college campuses. Public marches and rallies were held, too. In April 1965, the SDS organized a march on Washington, D.C., that drew more than 20,000 participants. In 1967 a rally at the Lincoln Memorial led to a march on the Pentagon. Federal marshals and soldiers formed a line outside the Pentagon to hold the protesters at bay. By 1968 the country seemed to be divided between hawks—people who wanted the United States to stay and fight—and doves—people who wanted the United States to withdraw from Vietnam.

★ TASK

You are going to create a political cartoon strip that shows how different people reacted to the Vietnam War. Include frames showing the positions taken by the following people: an African American youth living in an inner city, a college student who is against the war, a general who is a hawk, an American prisoner of war in North Vietnam, and a couple whose son is fighting in South Vietnam. Dialogue or captions should accompany each frame of your cartoon strip.

★ AUDIENCE

Readers of the cartoon strip are your intended audience.

★ PURPOSE

The purpose of this activity is to illustrate the different viewpoints that Americans held concerning the Vietnam War. The combination of these different views should provide a deeper understanding of American history during that time period.

★ **Performance Assessment Activity 30** (continued)

⊠ PROCEDURES

1. Review the background information concerning the Vietnam War and the impact that war had on the American people.

2. Do further research about the position of each of the characters or groups you will depict. List each character, that character's point of view, and the reasons for that point of view on the lines below.

_____

_____

_____

_____

_____

3. Create a line of dialogue or a caption to use in each cartoon frame. The dialogue should highlight the position held by each character. Make notes on the following lines.

_____

_____

_____

_____

4. Investigate newspapers and magazines for examples of political cartoons and cartoon strips. You may use ideas from these in your cartoon strip.

5. Use the lines below to make notes on the physical characteristics of the individuals you include in your cartoon strip. Remember that exaggeration of certain features and the use of familiar symbols are often used in political cartoon strips.

_____

_____

_____

6. Make a rough draft of your cartoon strip, including written elements and rough sketches. Check to make sure that the cartoon illustrates the points you want to make.

7. Exchange cartoons with a classmate for a peer review.

8. Make your final cartoon strip. Post your cartoon strip on a bulletin board.

⊠ ASSESSMENT

1. Use the Assessment Lists suggested to evaluate your political cartoon strip.

2. Check to see that you have included all elements; improve as needed.

3. Complete a final self-assessment of your work before you share it.

The American Vision

★ Performance Assessment Activity 31

Use with Chapter 31

Peace, Power, Freedom, Happiness

★ BACKGROUND

The 1960s was one of the most tumultuous and chaotic decades in American history. Along with all the political and economic changes and the events surrounding the struggle for civil rights, the youths of America were challenging America's social system and conventional middle-class values. By the early 1960s, many young people had become more active in social causes. The rapid increase in college enrollment allowed young people to meet and bond with others who shared their thoughts and feelings about society and the future. Although many American youths wanted to challenge the system and work to improve it, others wanted to leave the system and build their own society. These youths, who often dressed flamboyantly and wore their hair long, became known as the counterculture. Commonly called "hippies," people in the counterculture wanted to live their lives closer to nature and to be more open to love, empathy, and tolerance. Many of them saw drugs such as marijuana and LSD as being the key to finding inner peace. Some hippies "dropped out" and lived in communes—group living arrangements where members shared everything and worked together. However, the counterculture movement began to deteriorate after a few years. Some of the newcomers to the movement did not always understand the original ideas. Drug problems became more prevalent, and criminal activity became all too frequent. For the most part, the young men and women who created the counterculture gradually returned to American society. The counterculture movement, though, left its imprint on American culture—particularly with its music. The music of the Beatles, the Rolling Stones, Stevie Wonder, Janis Joplin, Bob Dylan, and Jimi Hendrix, among many others, is still popular today.

★ TASK

You are a writer for *Rolling Stone* magazine. Your editor has asked you to write an article about the August 1969 Woodstock music festival. Your article, which will be published on the *Rolling Stone* Web site, should include the names of people and groups who performed there, the names of songs that were played, the goals of the performers, and any other interesting facts about the festival that you can find. Your article may include photos and first-hand accounts from people who attended.

★ AUDIENCE

Visitors to the Web site are your intended audience.

★ PURPOSE

The purpose of this activity is to inform readers about the Woodstock festival and its goals, and to create an article worthy of publication on the Web.

★ Performance Assessment Activity 31 (continued)

★ PROCEDURES

1. Gather information on the August 1969 festival at Woodstock. Consult as many primary sources as you can. Look for personal accounts and other historical information in the library.

2. Make an outline of your article on the lines below. Your article should begin by briefly describing the location of the festival.

_____

_____

_____

_____

_____

_____

_____

_____

_____

_____

_____

_____

3. Write a title for your article on the line below.

_____

4. Find photos that relate to your article. Write a caption for each photo on the lines below.

_____

_____

_____

_____

5. Write a rough draft of your article.

6. Give your article to a classmate for comments and suggestions. Ask your classmate if any part of the article is unclear.

7. Write your final article after making any necessary revisions.

★ ASSESSMENT

1. Use the Assessment Lists suggested to evaluate your Web article.

2. Check to see that you have included all elements; improve as needed.

3. Complete a final self-assessment of your work before you share it.

★ Performance Assessment Activity 32

Use with Chapter 32

The 1970s

★ BACKGROUND

By the time the 1970s arrived, Americans who had experienced the Watergate scandal, the Vietnam War, and economic problems were ready to get on with their lives. Americans seemed to grow more self-obsessed in their quest for personal fulfillment. Activities like yoga, martial arts, and chanting to achieve fuller spiritual awareness became popular, and many people professed a belief in the healing powers of crystals and gemstones. New religions such as the Hare Krishna movement and the Unification Church spawned rumors of cults. Mystical teachers known as gurus encouraged their followers to lead lives based on health and harmony. Traditional values were changing again. The divorce rate doubled, the birthrate fell, and women began viewing their roles as wives and mothers more critically. Popular entertainment reflected these changes. Television shows took on such formerly taboo subjects as racism, poverty, and abortion. Shows like *All in the Family*, *The Jeffersons*, and *Good Times* tried to present American life in as unvarnished a view as possible. Although the realism was often compromised, television viewers had never before seen these subjects treated in such a way. The rock and roll music of the 1960s gave way to disco music and music that was less political in nature. In addition to disco music and disco dancing, Americans immersed themselves in several fads and fashions. Skateboards, mood rings, CB radios, and personalized T-shirts became popular. The fitness craze became another popular trend, as Americans turned to exercise to improve the way they felt and the way they looked. Aerobic exercise in particular became quite popular. By the end of the 1970s, these fads and trends began to fade.

★ TASK

Your group has been asked by the producers of a popular television quiz show to write a series of questions and answers for their program. Your questions and answers will deal with American culture during the 1970s. Your questions and answers will be based on the following five categories: fads and fashions, religion, television shows and movies, music, and traditional American values. You will submit a list of your questions and answers to the producers, who will include them in the category "The 1970s" for their quiz show.

★ AUDIENCE

Television viewers and quiz show participants are your intended audience.

★ PURPOSE

The purpose of this activity is to work with a group to highlight what was important in American culture in the 1970s.

★ Performance Assessment Activity 32 (continued)

✪ PROCEDURES

1. Review information about American culture during the 1970s. Consult the library or Internet resources for as many accounts as you can find.

2. Assign each member of your group one of the five categories of questions. Write the assignments on the following lines.

_____

_____

_____

_____

3. On the following lines, list at least five questions that you could ask in your assigned category. Write the answer underneath each question.

_____

_____

_____

_____

_____

_____

_____

_____

_____

_____

_____

4. Work within your group to answer each of the questions. If a question does not seem to be clear, ask the group for suggestions. Participate in giving feedback on the questions.

5. Make a final list of your questions and answers. Work in your group to create a bank of at least 25 questions, although it may contain more. In a simulated TV game show, ask the members of your class to answer as many of your questions as they can.

✪ ASSESSMENT

1. Use the Assessment Lists suggested to evaluate your cooperative group management plan in writing the quiz questions.

2. Check to see that you have included all elements; improve as needed.

3. Complete a final self-assessment of your work before you share it.

★ Performance Assessment Activity 33

Use with Chapter 33

Conservative or Liberal?

✪ BACKGROUND

People who call themselves liberals believe in several basic ideals. They believe that the government should control the economy so that ordinary citizens can be protected from the power of large corporations and very wealthy individuals. Liberals believe that the government should play a very active role in helping disadvantaged Americans. They believe this help should come through social programs and by higher taxes placed on the wealthy. Liberals are strong supporters of free speech and privacy, and they are opposed to government endorsing any religious beliefs or practices. Liberals believe that a diverse society made up of many different races, cultures, and ethnic groups tends to be more creative and energetic than a society that is more homogenous.

Conservatives, like liberals, want to solve social problems and help the disadvantaged. However, conservatives believe that if the government regulates the economy, the economy will become less efficient. If the economy is less efficient, conservatives believe that the result will be less overall wealth and more people living in poverty. They think that people and businesses should be free to make their own economic choices. Conservatives generally oppose high taxes and government programs that give benefits to the disadvantaged. They believe that this takes away people's incentive to work hard. Many conservatives also believe that religion plays a big part in day-to-day life, and they think that government and religious faith should not be kept entirely separate. Most conservatives do not believe that social problems are caused by the economic system. They view most social problems as problems of morality and character. In 1980 Ronald Reagan, a strong conservative, was elected president, and American society moved in a more conservative direction. Conservatives and liberals found themselves at odds on some of the major issues of the day.

✪ TASK

You are going to write a position paper. The topic of your paper will be one of the problems faced by American society. You may choose drugs and violence, poverty, the Equal Rights Amendment (ERA), or any other topic about which you feel strongly. You will take either the liberal or the conservative viewpoint and defend that viewpoint in a written position paper. You will read your paper aloud.

✪ AUDIENCE

The members of your class are your intended audience.

✪ PURPOSE

The purpose of this activity is to persuade your classmates that your approach to the problem is the best approach for America.

★ Performance Assessment Activity 33 (continued)

★ PROCEDURES

1. Choose a problem facing American society that is of particular interest to you. This problem may concern drugs and violence, poverty, the Equal Rights Amendment, or any other topic about which you feel strongly. Write your topic on the following line.

    _____

2. Conduct research on your topic. Locate information concerning both the conservative and the liberal views of this problem. Use the following lines to make notes.

    _____
    _____
    _____
    _____
    _____

3. Decide whether you will defend the conservative or the liberal point of view. Do further research on that view, and make notes on the following lines.

    _____
    _____
    _____
    _____

4. On the lines below, write an outline of your paper.

    _____
    _____
    _____
    _____
    _____
    _____

5. Make a draft of your position paper, using language and reasoning that will appeal to your audience. Give your draft to a classmate for comments and suggestions.

6. Write the final draft of your position paper, incorporating any necessary revisions. Read your paper aloud to your classmates.

★ ASSESSMENT

1. Use the Assessment Lists suggested to evaluate your position paper.

2. Check to see that you have included all elements; improve as needed.

3. Complete a final self-assessment of your work before you share it.

★ Performance Assessment Activity 34

Use with Chapter 34

William Jefferson Clinton

★ BACKGROUND

William Jefferson Clinton, a "new Democrat," won the 1992 presidential race against the incumbent Republican president, George Bush, and Reform Party candidate H. Ross Perot. Although his administration inherited a troubled economy, Clinton was able to stimulate the economy by raising taxes and holding back federal spending. Under Clinton, the 1990s broke all records for economic growth. Although the economy greatly improved, Clinton's first years in office were shaky. A major health care initiative, spearheaded by First Lady Hillary Rodham Clinton, failed. The failure of the health care reform initiative and higher taxes caused the Republicans, led by Newt Gingrich of Georgia, to announce a "Contract with America." This contract proposed 10 major changes, including lowering taxes, tougher anticrime laws, and limits on congressional terms. As a result, the Republicans gained 54 House seats and 9 Senate seats, which gave them a majority in both houses of Congress. Congress and the president then clashed over the federal budget. A compromise was finally reached.

Clinton's second term as president focused on children and education. Clinton advocated increased student loans and grants to help low-income children go to college, and he also persuaded Congress to create AmeriCorps. AmeriCorps was a program designed to help students earn tuition by cleaning up the environment and improving low-income housing. In spite of Clinton's accomplishments, two events led to his impeachment. One was his involvement in a failed real estate venture called Whitewater. An independent prosecutor, Kenneth Starr, was appointed to investigate the president's alleged misconduct. Starr eventually expanded his investigation into other issues, including Clinton's involvement with a White House intern. Although the House voted to impeach Clinton, he was acquitted of the charges.

★ TASK

You will interview people about their opinions on Bill Clinton and his presidency. You will prepare a list of questions to ask your subjects. Questions should focus on Clinton's presidential style, his character, foreign and domestic policies, and efforts to improve the economy. You may ask additional questions of your choice.

★ AUDIENCE

Your interview subjects and the members of your class are your intended audience.

★ PURPOSE

The purpose of your interview is to provide an informative survey of people's opinions about President Bill Clinton and his policies.

★ **Performance Assessment Activity 34** (continued)

☒ PROCEDURES

1. Review information about Bill Clinton's presidency. Research Clinton's foreign and domestic policies and his handling of the national economy. You may also include issues of your choice, such as his handling of the AIDS epidemic, immigration, and welfare. Make notes on the following lines.

_____

_____

_____

_____

_____

2. Research issues dealing with Clinton's presidential style and his character. Make notes on the following lines.

_____

_____

_____

_____

3. Make a list of the questions you will ask. Write them on the following lines.

_____

_____

_____

_____

_____

_____

4. Think about how many interviews you will conduct and the type of people you will interview. Aim for a cross section of individuals, such as young people and senior citizens, Democrats and Republicans, and people of different races. Contact the people you want to interview and set up an appointment.

5. Conduct your interviews. Use a tape recorder if possible.

6. Summarize your interviews in a two- or three-page written report.

7. Present the summary of your report to your classmates.

☒ ASSESSMENT

1. Use the Assessment Lists suggested to evaluate your interviews.

2. Check to see that you have included all elements; improve as needed.

3. Complete a final self-assessment of your work before you share it.

The American Vision

Use with Activities 2, 9, 11, 16, 24, 25, and 26.

S   The presentation, monologue, song, or skit is eloquent. Creativity is clearly present. The speaker or singer shows a flair for communicating with the audience, making eye contact with the entire audience. The speaker's or singer's dress and posture are appropriate. The speaker or singer communicates with confidence and ease. Visual aids are excellent, and are incorporated flawlessly with the oral presentation, monologue, or skit. There are clear and smooth transitions between speaking points. The speaker or singer involves the audience in some active way.

T   The presenter speaks or sings in a clear voice and at an appropriate rate of speed. The speaker or singer is interesting, enthusiastic, and makes eye contact with the entire audience. The presentation, monologue, song, or skit is well-organized. A strong central theme is supported by main ideas. Details and examples clarify the main ideas. The speaker or singer clearly understands the subject matter. Visual aids, if used, are well-done and make the presentation more interesting and meaningful.

U   The presentation, monologue, song, or skit is similar to one receiving a rating of **T,** except there are one or two important elements that are less polished, or there is an element omitted.

V   The presentation, monologue, song, or skit is similar to one receiving a rating of **W,** except there are one or two important elements that are relatively well-done.

W   The presenter or singer is difficult to hear and/or speaks at an incorrect rate of speed. The speaker or singer lacks interest or enthusiasm, appearing to read the presentation. Eye contact is poor or spotty. The speaker or singer is not well-groomed. The presentation lacks organization. Details or examples are insufficient or inappropriate. Some information may be incomplete or inaccurate. It is not clear that the speaker understands the subject matter. Visual aids are poorly done and/or do not enhance the information.

X   The presentation, monologue, song, or skit is very poorly organized and delivered.

Use with Activities 2, 9, 11, 16, 24, 25, and 26.

ELEMENT ASSIGNMENT	POINTS POSSIBLE	ASSESSMENT SELF	TEACHER
1. Everyone can hear the speaker or singer clearly.	_____	_____	_____
2. The speaker or singer is enthusiastic.	_____	_____	_____
3. The presenter's pace is even.	_____	_____	_____
4. The presenter makes eye contact with individuals throughout the audience.	_____	_____	_____
5. The presenter is dressed appropriately, is well-groomed, and has excellent posture.	_____	_____	_____
6. The presentation, monologue, song, or skit is well-organized.	_____	_____	_____
7. The main ideas support the theme.	_____	_____	_____
8. There are enough details to support the main ideas.	_____	_____	_____
9. The presenter knows the subject.	_____	_____	_____
10. Visual aids, if used, are well-done.	_____	_____	_____
11. The presenter involves the audience.	_____	_____	_____
12. The length is appropriate.	_____	_____	_____
13. The presentation, monologue, song, or skit communicates effectively.	_____	_____	_____
Total	_____	_____	_____

Use with Activities 1, 3, 17, and 19.

S The map, display, or chart is outstanding. It is so attractive, creative, interesting, and compelling that the audience will enjoy viewing it again and again. The information presented is technically accurate. The ideas are presented clearly, and flow logically from one to the next. The artistic and technical aspects of the project are excellent.

T The map, display, or chart immediately catches your eye through the use of humor, design, or other strategies. The message is clear and accurate. Concepts are appropriately and accurately presented. The design is well thought out and the visual elements are organized and effective. The map, display, or chart seems neither too crowded nor too scanty. The illustrations, text, and other design elements combine neatly and effectively.

U The map, display, or chart is similar to the one receiving a rating of **T,** except one or two important elements are not consistent with the over-all quality of the display.

V The map, display, or chart is similar to the one receiving a rating of **W,** except there are one or two important elements that are well-done.

W The map, display, or chart is not interesting and/or appealing. Important concepts are unclear. Information is missing or incorrect. The design is cluttered and/or unorganized. The mix of illustrations, text, and other design elements does not accomplish the intended purpose. The project is messy.

X The map, display, or chart is very poorly done.

Use with Activities 1, 3, 17, and 19.

ELEMENT ASSIGNMENT	POINTS POSSIBLE	ASSESSMENT SELF	ASSESSMENT TEACHER
1. The map, display, or chart is attractive, creative, and interesting.	_____	_____	_____
2. The ideas are presented clearly.	_____	_____	_____
3. The creator uses humor, interesting design, or other features to catch the eye.	_____	_____	_____
4. The map, display, or chart message is clear.	_____	_____	_____
5. Information is appropriate and accurate.	_____	_____	_____
6. The map, display, or chart does not appear too full or too empty.	_____	_____	_____
7. The illustrations, text, and other design elements work well together.	_____	_____	_____
8. The overall appearance is neat and presentable.	_____	_____	_____
Total	_____	_____	_____

Use with Activities 4, 8, 12, 15, and 27.

S   The diary, short story, memorandum, or letter is exceptionally insight-ful and comprehensive. The student has demonstrated remarkable initiative and diligence in the project, including clippings and informa-tion from a variety of sources. The diary, short story, memorandum, or letter shows that the student has thoughtfully and diligently worked at interpreting history. The diary, short story, memorandum, or letter demonstrates an understanding of local, regional, and global history. Comments reflect a desire to learn about other regions and cultures. The diary, short story, memorandum, or letter is impeccable in appearance.

T   The diary, short story, memorandum, or letter is well-organized. The student has demonstrated reasonable initiative and diligence in the project by including a variety of sources and interpreting them with insight. Personal experiences are recorded and feelings explored with care. Reflection and personal growth are evident. The diary, short story, memorandum, or letter is very neat and presentable.

U   The diary, short story, memorandum, or letter is similar to the one receiving a rating of **T,** except there are one or two important elements that are not excellent, or the diary, short story, memorandum, or letter is too short.

V   The diary, short story, memorandum, or letter is similar to the one receiving a rating of **W,** except there are one or two important elements that are relatively well-done.

W   The student's diary, short story, memorandum, or letter is incomplete and/or disorganized. There is little evidence of independent effort. It appears that the student worked inconsistently and has not supplied adequate descriptions of events or impressions. There is no real attempt to explore personal feelings. Statements indicating reflection and evidence of personal growth are inadequate or missing.

X   All elements of the diary, short story, memorandum, or letter are very poorly done.

Use with Activities 4, 8, 12, 15, and 27.

ELEMENT ASSIGNMENT	POINTS POSSIBLE	ASSESSMENT SELF	TEACHER
1. The diary, short story, memorandum, or letter is neatly organized and presented.	_____	_____	_____
2. The diary, short story, memorandum, or letter contains dated entries in the correct order, if appropriate.	_____	_____	_____
3. The diary, short story, memorandum, or letter includes a variety of information.	_____	_____	_____
4. Descriptions of current events related to history are recorded.	_____	_____	_____
5. Personal experiences and feelings about history are included, if appropriate.	_____	_____	_____
6. The diary, short story, memorandum, or letter is thoughtful and shows evidence of personal growth as a learner.	_____	_____	_____
7. The diary, short story, memorandum, or letter shows an interest in learning more about history.	_____	_____	_____
Total	_____	_____	_____

Use with Activities 5, 26, 29, and 32.

S   The plan is exceptional and could serve as an example of excellent work. The group members have simulated, to an extraordinary degree, how teamwork is used in the larger world to achieve a common goal.

T   The plan is excellent. It encourages full, enthusiastic participation and diverse ideas. The purpose statement and audience description reflect a thorough understanding of the goal. Care and foresight in planning encourages equitable task distribution and individual accountability. The plan sets realistic time frames for completion of individual tasks and requires minimal adjustment. The presentation assures the fullest possible participation and gives full credit for contributions. The plan is neat.

U   The work is generally as good as one receiving a rating of **T,** but it is uneven with some less-developed elements.

V   The work is similar to that receiving a rating of **W,** but it has one or two areas that are better developed.

W   The plan does not accomplish its purpose. Full participation is not evident, and a diversity of ideas does not emerge. The purpose statement is vague, and the audience description inadequate. Tasks are not equitable. Problems are unforeseen. Individual accountability is not clear, and the time frames are unrealistic. Unnecessary redistribution of tasks and adjustment of time frames disrupt the process. The plan does not allow for full participation or appropriate credit. The work is sloppy.

X   The plan is very poorly done in all respects.

★ Assessment List for a Cooperative Group Management Plan

Use with Activities 5, 26, 29, and 32.

ELEMENT ASSIGNMENT	POINTS POSSIBLE	ASSESSMENT SELF	TEACHER
1. Team members agree on a purpose statement and an audience description.	_____	_____	_____
2. Team members agree on a list of tasks required to achieve the goal.	_____	_____	_____
3. Team members agree on scheduled dates for checking progress toward the goal.	_____	_____	_____
4. Problems that might interfere with completion are identified and solved.	_____	_____	_____
5. Tasks are divided fairly.	_____	_____	_____
6. Each member has indicated approval of the planning phase by initialing beside his/her name on a printed list of group members.	_____	_____	_____

PROCESS

7. Team members agree on adjustments to individual tasks, if necessary, to maintain a fair division of labor.	_____	_____	_____

PRODUCT

8. Team members agree on a format for the presentation of the product.

a. Each member plays an active role in the presentation.	_____	_____	_____
b. Each member receives credit for his/her contribution.	_____	_____	_____

FINAL ANALYSIS

9. Each member has signed the final plan to indicate his/her approval of participation in the process and presentation.	_____	_____	_____
10. The management plan is neat and presentable.	_____	_____	_____
Total	_____	_____	_____

The American Vision

Use with Activities 5 and 29.

S   The presentation is exceptional. The text and characters use creativity and/or humor to send a clear message to the intended audience. Outstanding effort in preparing costumes, scenery, and props is obvious. Participants are poised and well-rehearsed. The presentation is organized, focuses on the topic, and is an appropriate length.

T   Overall, the presentation is excellent and communicates its message to the audience. The participants can be seen and heard. The information and dialogue are appropriate to the topic and audience. The characters are well-suited to the topic and are well-developed by the participants. The props add to the effectiveness of the presentation. The presentation is well organized.

U   The presentation is generally as good as one receiving a rating of **T,** but it is uneven with some less-developed elements.

V   The presentation is similar to that receiving a rating of **W,** but it has one or two areas that are better developed.

W   The presentation does not communicate the proposed message to the intended audience. The participants cannot be seen and/or heard. All characters may not be suited to the topic and/or be developed by the participants. The props are lacking or are distracting. The presentation is disorganized or unfocused and/or is too long or too short. Verbal and/or nonverbal information presented in the skit is not accurate.

X   The presentation is very poor in all respects.

Use with Activities 5 and 29.

ELEMENT ASSIGNMENT	POINTS POSSIBLE	ASSESSMENT SELF	TEACHER
1. The entire audience can hear the speakers.	_____	_____	_____
2. The dialogue is appropriate to both the topic and the audience.	_____	_____	_____
3. The characters are suitable for the topic of the presentation.	_____	_____	_____
4. The participants develop the characters well.	_____	_____	_____
5. The props used in the presentation add to the interest and message.	_____	_____	_____
6. Everyone can see the presentation.	_____	_____	_____
7. The presentation is organized and focused.	_____	_____	_____
8. The information in the presentation, both spoken and nonspoken, is accurate and appropriate.	_____	_____	_____
9. The presentation is an appropriate length.	_____	_____	_____
Total	_____	_____	_____

Use with Activities 6, 7, 20, 21, 23, and 31.

S   The article or ad is exceptionally insightful and comprehensive. It is eloquent, informative, and achieves its purpose with the intended audience. The introduction describes what the author proposes to say, provides a context for the topic, and lays out a style and organizational plan. Each paragraph has a clear topic sentence that is supported by details that work together to develop the theme. All facts are correct. Graphic elements are included. The artistic and technical aspects of the article or ad are excellent. Writing mechanics are flawless.

T   The article or ad is well-organized, logically developed, and engaging. The writer understands the topic, and has organized the material skillfully. The article or ad is concise, with excellent grammar and mechanics. The article flows from one concept to the next in an orderly fashion. All resource materials are properly referenced. The title of the article or ad is appropriate and contributes to the overall quality of the project. The article or ad is neat and presentable.

U   The article or ad is almost as good as that receiving a rating of **T,** but it is uneven with some missing or less-developed elements.

V   The article or ad is similar to that receiving a rating of **W,** but it has one or two important elements that are better developed.

W   The article or ad is incomplete and/or disorganized. There is little evidence of independent effort. The purpose of the article or ad is not clear. It appears that the student worked inconsistently and has not supplied adequate descriptions of events or impressions. Some paragraphs do not have main ideas and/or supporting details. Some information is inaccurate, and several errors in grammar and/or mechanics are present. The paper is messy.

X   The article or ad is very poorly done.

Use with Activities 6, 7, 20, 21, 23, and 31.

ELEMENT ASSIGNMENT	POINTS POSSIBLE	ASSESSMENT SELF	TEACHER
1. The topic is clear, and the introduction is effective.	_____	_____	_____
2. The title is appropriate and interesting.	_____	_____	_____
3. The introduction is strong and clear.	_____	_____	_____
4. Each paragraph has a topic sentence that is supported by details.	_____	_____	_____
5. Graphic elements are included, appropriate, and well-drawn.	_____	_____	_____
6. All facts are correct.	_____	_____	_____
7. The author clearly demonstrates essential knowledge of the topic.	_____	_____	_____
8. The conclusion shows that the author has kept the purpose of the project in mind.	_____	_____	_____
9. Spelling and grammar are correct.	_____	_____	_____
10. The article or ad is very neat and presentable.	_____	_____	_____
Total	_____	_____	_____

Use with Activities 10, 14, 18, 28, and 30.

S The political cartoon, pamphlet, or handbill is outstanding. It is exceptionally insightful and comprehensive. The student has demonstrated remarkable initiative and diligence in the project and has used information drawn from a variety of sources. The artistic and technical aspects of the project are excellent. Ideas are presented clearly and flow logically from one to the next. The project shows that the student has thoughtfully worked at interpreting the role of history in his or her life.

T The project immediately catches your eye through the use of humor, design, or other strategies. The message is clear and the concepts are appropriately and accurately presented. The design is well thought out and the visual elements are organized and effective. The illustrations, text, and other design elements combine neatly and effectively.

U The project is almost as good as that receiving a rating of **T,** but it is uneven with some missing or less-developed elements.

V The project is similar to that receiving a rating of **W,** but it has one or two important elements that are better developed.

W The project is not interesting and/or appealing. Important concepts are unclear. Information is missing or incorrect. The design is cluttered and/or unorganized. The mix of illustrations, text, and other design elements does not accomplish the intended purpose. There is little evidence of independent effort. Several errors in grammar and mechanics are evident. The project is messy.

X The project is very poorly done.

Use with Activities 10, 14, 18, 28, and 30.

ELEMENT ASSIGNMENT	POINTS POSSIBLE	ASSESSMENT SELF	TEACHER
1. The project is attractive, creative, and interesting.	_____	_____	_____
2. The project is neatly organized and presented.	_____	_____	_____
3. The ideas are presented clearly.	_____	_____	_____
4. The student uses humor, interesting design, or other features to catch the eye.	_____	_____	_____
5. The message of the project is clear.	_____	_____	_____
6. Information is appropriate and accurate.	_____	_____	_____
7. The illustrations, text, and other design elements work well together.	_____	_____	_____
8. The project is thoughtful and shows evidence of personal growth as a learner.	_____	_____	_____
9. The overall appearance is neat and presentable.	_____	_____	_____
Total	_____	_____	_____

Use with Activities 13 and 33.

S The paper is exceptional in all elements. It is eloquent, informative, and achieves its purpose with the intended audience. A thesis statement clearly defines the topic. The introduction describes what the author proposes to say (or prove), provides a context for the topic, and lays out a style and organizational plan. Each paragraph has a clear topic sentence and appropriate supporting details that work together to develop the thesis. All facts are correct. The conclusion effectively demonstrates that the author proved what was stated in the thesis. Writing mechanics are flawless.

T The paper is evenly well-organized, logically developed, and engaging. The writer understands the topic, and has organized the material skill-fully. The paper is concise with excellent grammar and mechanics. The author's mastery of the concepts is evident. All resource materials are properly referenced. The paper is neat and presentable.

U The paper is almost as good as that receiving a rating of **T,** but it is uneven with some missing or less-developed elements.

V The paper is similar to that receiving a rating of **W,** but it has one or two important elements that are better developed.

W The paper is unorganized and poorly developed. The thesis statement is unclear. The introduction fails to explain the purpose of the paper, context for the thesis, and/or provide an organization plan for this paper. Some paragraphs do not have main ideas and/or supporting details. Some information is inaccurate, the arguments unconvincing. Several errors in grammar and/or mechanics are present. Sources of information are not cited. The paper is messy.

X The book review, research report, or position paper is extremely weak in all areas.

Use with Activities 13 and 33.

ELEMENT ASSIGNMENT	POINTS POSSIBLE	ASSESSMENT	
		SELF	TEACHER
1. The topic is clear and the introduction effective.	_____	_____	_____
2. A thesis statement clearly defines the topic.	_____	_____	_____
3. The body of the paper is organized into paragraphs with clear main ideas and appropriate supporting details.	_____	_____	_____
4. The author clearly demonstrates essential knowledge of the topic.	_____	_____	_____
5. The conclusion shows that the author has kept the paper's purpose in mind.	_____	_____	_____
6. The author's own thinking is the focus of this report.	_____	_____	_____
7. The author accurately and completely references all sources of information.	_____	_____	_____
8. Visual aids, such as graphs or diagrams, if used, help explain the information.	_____	_____	_____
9. Spelling and grammar are correct.	_____	_____	_____
10. The report is very neat and presentable.	_____	_____	_____
Total	_____	_____	_____

Use with Activity 22.

S   The photos chosen represent the historical era or region well. The accompanying text is well written. Obvious research has resulted in an informative and engaging narrative. The photos cleverly illustrate the narrative and are well-placed. The oral delivery of the presentation (if done) is smooth and well rehearsed.

T   The photo essay is creative and well-done. The text features factual information in a straightforward way. The photos chosen show creativity and a sensitivity to pacing with the text. The oral presentation (if done) is interesting, thought provoking, and entertaining. Details and examples clarify the main ideas. The student clearly understands the subject.

U   The presentation is similar to one receiving a rating of **T**, except there are one or two important elements that are less polished, or there is an element omitted.

V   The presentation is similar to one receiving a rating of **W**, except there are one or two important elements that are relatively well-done.

W   The presentation lacks focus. There is weakness in the content of the text. The photos are poorly presented, poorly described, or inappropriate for the presentation. The oral delivery, if done, is ineffective. Major themes are missing or poorly developed.

X   The presentation is very poorly organized and delivered.

Use with Activity 22.

ELEMENT ASSIGNMENT	POINTS POSSIBLE	ASSESSMENT SELF	TEACHER
1. The subject is well-researched.	_____	_____	_____
2. The text follows a logical order.	_____	_____	_____
3. The photos and text work well together to create a story.	_____	_____	_____
4. The length is appropriate.	_____	_____	_____
5. The main ideas support the theme.	_____	_____	_____
6. There are enough details to support the main ideas.	_____	_____	_____
7. The presentation is both informative and entertaining.	_____	_____	_____
8. Photos chosen are appropriate to the topic and are well-done.	_____	_____	_____
9. The oral presentation is smooth and well-rehearsed.	_____	_____	_____
10. The student knows the subject.	_____	_____	_____
11. The presenter communicates effectively.	_____	_____	_____
Total	_____	_____	_____

Use with Activity 34.

S The interview questions are exceptional in all elements. Questions show a superlative grasp of recent history. The questions are organized and focused and easily fall into a logical pattern. Questions have been written in a manner that draws complete and detailed comments from those persons being interviewed. Practically none of the questions are short-answer. The written questions are formatted in a way that will make written responses to the interview (if appropriate) easy. Writing mechanics are flawless.

T The student's grasp of the subject matter is evident from reading the interview questions. Questions are well-organized. Few of the questions are short-answer questions. The written questions are formatted in a way that will make written responses (if appropriate) easy. The questions are neat and presentable.

U The interview questions are almost as good as those receiving a rating of **T**, but they are uneven with some missing or less-developed elements.

V The interview questions are similar to those receiving a rating of **W**, but they have one or two important elements that are better developed.

W It is not clear that the student understands the subject matter or the assignment. The interview questions are poorly developed and disorganized. Most of the questions are short-answer questions. Questions are presented in such a way that the person responding to the interview is unable to express his/her opinions. Several errors in grammar and/or mechanics are present. The paper is messy.

X The interview questions are very poorly prepared and extremely weak in all areas.

Use with Activity 34.

ELEMENT ASSIGNMENT	POINTS POSSIBLE	ASSESSMENT SELF	TEACHER
1. Questions chosen demonstrate a thorough grasp of the subject matter.	_____	_____	_____
2. Questions are well-organized and easily fall into a logical pattern.	_____	_____	_____
3. The questions are written to draw complete and detailed answers from the subject(s) of the interview.	_____	_____	_____
4. Personal experiences and feelings about history are included.	_____	_____	_____
5. The format of the interview is appropriate.	_____	_____	_____
6. Spelling and grammar are correct.	_____	_____	_____
7. The questions are very neat and presentable.	_____	_____	_____
Total	_____	_____	_____